THE BILLY BEST STORY

THE BILLY BEST STORY

Beating Cancer
with Alternative Medicine

By Billy Best
as told to Linda Conti

Sandcastle
MEMOIRS

Front cover photo: Julia Cumes, juliacumesphoto.com, taken at Coast
Guard Beach, Cape Cod National Seashore, Eastham, MA.

This book is for informational purposes only. It is not intended to
diagnose, prevent or treat any disease and should not be considered as a
substitute for consultation with a licensed health care professional.

Sandcastle
MEMOIRS

SandcastleMemoirs.com
ISBN 978-0-9854970-0-2

For Mom and Dad

Reflecting back on all that's happened in my life, I am blessed that you were always there for me, no matter what. You raised me, loved me, suffered with me, and celebrated with me. You helped guide me to be the man I am today.

How foolish it was of me to think I could run away to die alone. You persevered and you rescued me.

I wish you joy in your hearts. I love you both.

ACKNOWLEDGEMENTS

For over ten years, I worked on and off to get this book written. It would still be on my list of things to do for another decade if I didn't have Maya in my life to support and encourage me. Thank you for helping me to check this one off.

Thank you to everyone mentioned in the story for helping me escape, hide out, come home, or get better. I couldn't have done it without the combined effort from all of you. It's impossible for me to list everyone here who has helped me and made a difference in my life over the years, but here is at least a partial attempt.

Thank you to...

Richard Acken for telling me about 714X and inviting me into your home.

Charlie Pixley for all that you did for me.

The media for getting the story out there and being such a significant part of my return home.

All the people who, after hearing about my story, took time out of their day to write or call and share information about other ways I could treat my cancer.

Everyone in Texas who looked out for me.

My family for not giving up on me, even after all the pain I caused them.

Kevin and Angel for helping me early on when I began writing this book.

Martha and Rifat Chaprut and family

Kevin P. Miller

Jen at the Patriot Ledger

Gaston Naessens for inventing the therapy that saved my life, and the rest of the staff in Canada who continue to be so gracious.

Katie Hartley and Mike Panarelli for sharing their incredible stories of survival.

Linda Conti for being in the right place at the right time. I could not see myself working with anyone else on this project. I can't wait to have another story to tell with you.

Billy Best

ACKNOWLEDGEMENTS

There were several people who made significant contributions to this story by helping me with their meticulous proofing, tremendous suggestions and honest reviews.

Thank you to my sister, Sue Traynor, and my friends, Kimberly White, Corey Barrette, Serena Kilawee, Jamie Ghetti, and Ellen Griffin. I am grateful to all of them for their time and generosity.

A big thank you goes out to Julia Cumes for her gorgeous photography. She helped make my vision a stunning reality.

Heartfelt thanks to my husband, Domenico, for always giving me his unwavering support and encouragement and for patiently listening to me talk non-stop about this project since it began!

I also want to recognize and thank the rest of my family and friends for indulging me. I think I've probably mentioned something about "the book" in every single conversation we've had over the past year.

Finally, special thanks to Billy for entrusting me with his story and for giving me this fantastic opportunity. Never before has work been this much fun.

Linda Conti
Sandcastle Memoirs

CONTENTS

CONTENTS

Listen to your heart, and have faith in what you hear.

MY BEGINNING

I WAS BORN in Stoughton, Massachusetts in March of 1978. My birth mother, Dawn, was seventeen at the time.

Many years later when I was finally fortunate to meet her, I learned a little bit about her life, as well as the story of my slightly rocky introduction into this world.

Dawn's own mother left their family when she was only four, and her father was suddenly faced with raising her and her siblings on his own. As he strained to meet the ever-growing needs of his children, many days proved to be a struggle for them all.

At the age of nine, Dawn decided to go live with her mother, and over the next several years she would bounce back and forth between her parents' homes until she eventually settled permanently with her father.

In her teens, Dawn was a self-described "wild child," a girl who posed a serious challenge to her single parent dad. As an adolescent, she managed to find the wrong crowd to hang with, and that – combined with her own family dynamic – had a significant impact on her tumultuous young life.

When she was sixteen, Dawn had a brief encounter with a slightly older man – a Native American man – and I was the unexpected result of that union. She never saw the man again, and he never knew that he had fathered a son.

During the first several weeks of my life, my grandfather witnessed his daughter's frustrated efforts to keep up with the constant demands of a tiny infant, confirming his suspicion that she was not nearly ready to take on this daunting responsibility. In addition to that, his own small home was already bursting at the seams, and it wasn't long before he announced to her that she would have to pack up her new son and move out.

As harsh as that seemed at the time, it was her father's only way of forcing Dawn to face the truth – that she had no ability or resources to properly care for a newborn child – and I desperately needed a good home.

Dawn knew then that she was about to pay a serious price for her indiscretion. When I was three months old, she tearfully surrendered me to foster care.

That scenario could have created years of instability for me – possibly being shuffled from one foster home to the next – but fortunately, it was a Godsend. At the age of seven months, I was adopted by my parents. With the two of them by my side, and my sister Jenny, who is a year older than I, our happy family was complete.

Over the years, we shared all of the usual growing-up-together experiences that parents and children do, with the busy routine typical of a family with two active kids. Our daily lives were saturated with work, school, sports and community, as we enjoyed the present and planned for the future.

At the age of sixteen, to all of our horror, I was diagnosed with Hodgkin's Lymphoma. This is my story of triumph over that cancer, using alternative treatments (714X, Essiac Tea), natural foods and natural products to strengthen my immune system and fight the disease from within.

Did my Native American heritage somehow subconsciously steer me away from the harsh chemotherapy and radiation therapy that was offered? I believe that's very possible. Did my belief system and my faith in a higher power protect me and show me the path to my healing? Absolutely.

By writing this book, it is not my intention to criticize, discredit or make judgments against any of the mainstream medical professionals, research, or treatments for cancer that we have in this country. It is simply my desire to share my story, and to let people know that there *are* real, natural, alternative treatments available for cancer – and that they worked for me.

This is my story of faith, resolve, and the ultimate success against the evil invader that once lurked inside my body. I hope that by reading my story, you will share my hope and be inspired to live each of your days to the fullest.

ONE

THE ACCIDENT

AS I LOOK back on the events that have shaped my life, there are many significant moments I can never forget – moments that have dramatically altered the direction of my fate. There is one that is so deeply etched in my memory, the mere thought of it rushes me swiftly back to that exact place and time so long ago, every detail still crystal clear.

It was November 14, 1992.

It was a cool, crisp mid-November Saturday. I was a healthy fourteen-year-old and a freshman in high school. My good friend, Alex, and I were starting construction on a skateboard ramp in my backyard.

I first learned how to skateboard years before as a young boy living in California. I was fascinated by it from the first moment, and when I realized I had the ability to not only stay on the board, but also to maneuver it, I was hooked. I was good at this! My enthusiasm quickly turned to passion.

I would jump on my board every minute of my free time – riding around the local neighborhoods for hours – always zeroing in on any place that had a large span of asphalt. I loved listening to the smooth sound of the rolling wheels as I would drop my board down and push off across the pavement. I learned and practiced all kinds of tricks, and it was my favorite thing to leap into the air and hear that *slap!* each time my board returned its wheels to the ground.

Over the years, I shared a close camaraderie with my fellow skateboarders, and I made a lot of friends through the sport. We would challenge each other to jump higher and turn tighter, and we would cheer on anyone who had outperformed the guy before him. Each of us would brag that some day we would be just like the pros.

Alex and I had already piled up the lumber in my yard. We just needed to pick up some bolts and screws from the store in the center of town. We hopped on our boards thinking it would be a quick trip. As it turned out, it took us longer than we expected and by the time we were headed back home, it was dark.

There were no sidewalks on the route, so we skated as far over to the side of the road as we could. Traffic was heavy and I was wearing dark clothing. I didn't feel safe not being able to see the cars coming from behind me; I knew they couldn't see me very well either.

As soon as there was an opportunity for us to cross, I motioned for Alex to follow me to the other side of the street. We both made it over and I felt much more comfortable. Now I could see cars as they were approaching, and if one of them looked like it was coming too near, I could veer off safely onto the shoulder of the road.

I was moving right along and I glanced back to check on Alex. He was falling behind again so I yelled to him.

"Come on! Hurry up!"

"I'm coming!" He waved me off.

"Well, hurry up," I yelled again. "We gotta get home."

In the next instant, before I could even turn my head fully around, I was hit.

I never saw it coming. In less than a split second, my right arm was hit by the side mirror of a one-ton dump truck. The truck had been traveling about forty-five miles per hour, and the impact sent me spinning.

Once I hit the ground, it took a few seconds for me to register what had happened. Alex jumped off his board and came running.

"Billy! Oh my God! Billy! Are you alright?"

I groaned, but managed to give him a small nod.

He crouched over me, keeping one eye on the traffic that was still rushing by us.

"We gotta get your feet out of the road!" Alex cried. I had landed with my back against a telephone pole, but my legs were stretched out, dangerously close to the passing cars.

"You're gonna get hit again," he said. "Can you get up?"

Somehow I managed to utter, "No."

I tried to move, but it was no use. I could wiggle my toes and move my head a little, so I knew I wasn't paralyzed, but I felt as if I had been glued to the ground. So I just lay there with my feet in the road.

The driver of the truck had pulled over and he came running towards us, waving a flashlight.

"Oh my God, kid! Are you okay? Gees, I never saw you!"

"Here!" he said to Alex, as he thrust the flashlight into Alex's hand. "Keep this light on him! I'll go for help."

He jumped back into his truck and raced off to the police station which was less than a mile away.

So there we were, the two of us, stuck on the side of the road – me unable to move, and Alex helpless to do anything about it.

As I lay there, I looked up and saw him pull a handful of gummy bears out of his pocket.

"Do you want some?" he gently asked me.

I thought to myself, "Ya, I do." I thought that must be a sign that probably nothing was too wrong with me. I figured I just got the wind knocked out.

Well, it didn't take long for me to realize my injuries were far more serious than I had imagined. The pain was creeping up on me. I felt a little panicked as I heard the approaching siren. This wasn't like one of those ambulances that you always hear in the distance, racing to an emergency for someone else. This one was coming straight for me.

I tried to stay calm.

The screaming siren got louder and louder and before I knew it, the ambulance was there with its lights blazing. One of the EMTs jumped out and immediately came to my side. He knelt down on the gravel where I lay.

"What's your name, son?"

"Billy."

"Okay, take it easy, Billy. Where does it hurt?"

I told him it was mostly my arm, but I couldn't move much of my body. They slid the backboard under me and lifted me into the back of the vehicle.

The first thing they did was cut off my shoelaces and remove my shoes and socks. One of them pinched my toes.

"Can you feel that?" he asked.

I could. That was a good sign. They saw that a ring on my left pinky finger had been crushed and was turning my finger blue.

"Let's get that off," one of them said. They grabbed an odd looking tool and snapped the metal ring, releasing my finger from the pressure.

Next was the jacket.

"Let's see his arm. Get the jacket off."

I was wearing a new jacket, one I really liked, and they were going to have to cut it. I didn't want it ruined.

"Wait, wait. Let me try," I said. I made a small attempt to take it off by myself but there was no way. The pain was now excruciating. They grabbed the shears and cut the jacket away from my arm. None of us knew it yet, but the sleeve of the jacket was pretty much the only thing holding my right forearm to my body. As they cut the sleeve away, my hand fell to the table. I saw my bones come out of my skin and my hand rested on the table next to my elbow. I heard one of the EMTs scream, "Oh my God!" That was the most scared I had ever been in my life.

"Am I gonna die?" I cried out. I was starting to lose control.

"No, no, Billy. Stay calm. You're gonna be okay."

"Am I in shock?"

"No, you're not in shock. You're gonna be fine, Billy. We're gonna get you over to the hospital."

"Can't you just knock me out?" I pleaded. "It's killing me."

"We can't, buddy. We need you to stay conscious."

They told me it would be okay if I wanted to scream.

So I did.

By the time we reached the emergency room at South Shore Hospital, the pain was unspeakable. The ER nurses splashed iodine on my wounds and gave me a dose of morphine. The first shot did absolutely nothing. I was being prepped for surgery when my mom and dad came running in.

"I'm sorry," I kept repeating to them. "I'm fine. I'm sorry. I really need something for the pain. Please get me something for the pain."

"They're bringing it, honey. They're bringing it." My mother tried desperately to console me.

The nurses gave me two more shots, but I still felt no relief. They apparently weren't allowed to give me any more, but it just wasn't enough. Mercifully, I blacked out.

I woke up to the sound of someone screaming, and opened my eyes just in time to see my sister running out of the recovery room. Jenny had been working at her first job at Brigham's Ice Cream in the Hanover Mall when she got the call. She was fifteen at the time. Whoever told her that I was in the hospital apparently didn't break the news to her very well, so the poor kid was hysterical. Instead of telling her in a careful, gentle way, "Your brother is fine, but he's in the hospital with a broken arm," a friend called her at work and said, "Jenny, your brother was hit by a truck!" When I awoke and heard her scream, I was shaking uncontrollably. I heard someone ask for a warm blanket, and then I passed out again.

I stayed in the hospital for about two weeks. During that time my right-hand fingers were swollen like sausages. The first few days in the hospital, I was completely out of it. My only activity was to push the morphine button. Whenever I woke

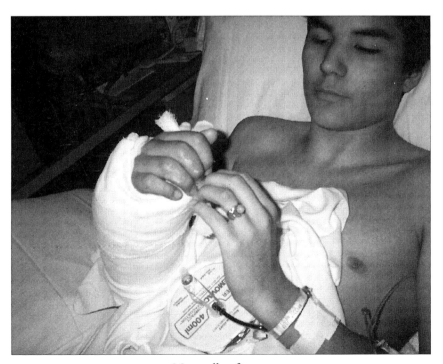

My swollen fingers

up, my first sensation was terrible pain, and if I pushed that button, the drug would knock me out again.

My mom was there, but I couldn't talk coherently; I had started hallucinating. When the doctors began to cut back on the drug, my threshold for pain was severely tested.

My right arm was wrapped in a huge bandage, with only my fingers sticking out. As the morphine wore off, my arm started to feel like it was on fire. My mom tried to cool it by putting a wet cloth over my hand, but the slightest touch brought agony. The only other thing she could do was use an eyedropper to drip ice water over my fingers. Each drop felt like I was being hit by a hammer, and yet strangely at the same time, the cool temperature provided me with some needed relief for my burning skin.

It took several days, but I finally started to feel a little better. A young nurse came in and explained what had happened to me. I had suffered a compound fracture from the collision; the truck mirror had hit my arm with such force that it was ripped free from its bolts. The trauma also did damage to the cartilage in my hand.

Next she explained the different wires and hoses going into my body. The wires for monitoring my heart rate, pulse and blood pressure didn't interest me much. The hose which contained my morphine meant almost everything. There was one more hose, the IV for fluids, and I would soon learn what that meant.

Later that night, I was watching TV when the nurse returned to my room.

"Just checking to see if you have gone to the bathroom yet?"

Frustrated in my hospital room

I told her that I didn't have to, but she said I needed to go soon.

"We keep pushing fluids into you," she explained, "and the fluids have to pass through. If you don't urinate by tomorrow morning, I am going to have to catheterize you. So do your best."

I wasn't having much luck with the bedpan because the drugs had clouded my senses. I wasn't sure what "catheterize" meant, but I was pretty sure it involved putting something somewhere I wouldn't like. Unfortunately, I ended up finding out all about it.

Eventually I managed to move from my bed into a wheelchair. My mother would push me around, but at first I was so weak, I could barely hold up my own head. Gradually,

I was taking less morphine and moving around more. Friends were able to come in and after two weeks had gone by, I was ready to leave and finish my recovery at home.

When I was finally able to return to school, I had stopped the morphine completely and they had switched me to Percocet. The pills were not as strong, but they were still potent, and I felt like my head was wrapped in a fog. I had to take four of them with my breakfast just to make the pain bearable for the ride to school.

Of course, the rumors from my accident were flying around. One was that I was hit by a Mack truck and that my arm was left with a reverse print of the distinctive hood ornament. I shuttled myself from class to class, sometimes feeling in a daze, answering the same questions over and over again.

"Yes, it hurt."

"No, I don't have 'Mack Truck' stamped on my arm."

"No, I'm not gonna quit skateboarding."

Months went by and it was time to have the cast removed. I used to watch reruns on TV of *The Twilight Zone* with Rod Serling, and I remember an episode where they operated on a character named "Pig Face" to correct his horrible disfigurement. They slowly, slowly peeled back the bandages to reveal what was underneath, only to discover that he was still grotesque and disgusting.

That is how I felt when I saw what was hiding beneath my cast. My heart sank when I saw what had become of my arm.

It looked like a shark had bitten it off, and that I had somehow wrestled my severed limb from the shark and sewn it back on.

The doctor gave me a new padded cast with straps to hold it in place. I could remove the cast for physical therapy or when taking a shower. On my first day back to school with this new cast, before even going to class, I ducked into a bathroom stall and locked the door behind me. I removed the straps holding the cast and looked down at my monstrous arm.

I don't know if it was my struggle to accept how awful it looked, if it was the months of living in a drug-induced haze, or the exhaustion of dealing with the constant pain, but I broke down and started to cry. Looking at the healing mess, I wondered how it could ever be right again. I tried to think about what my doctor had told me. He said he had a plan to perform multiple reconstructive surgeries. I would just have to wait it out.

Seven months after my accident, I went to Children's Hospital in Boston for the surgeries. It was June, 1993. Because my break was so severe, they called in the best orthopedic surgeon in the city.

The surgeon removed some bone from my hip and added it to my wrist. He secured it all in place with two metal plates and eleven screws. After a little more down time to recover and a few months of physical therapy, I was almost as good as new.

After the cast was removed this time, my arm was very sensitive where the plates remained under my skin. Months went by and it would still cause great pain if I tapped it against my desk or someone bumped me in the hall. The kids at school were all having to "tip toe" around me and I hated that. I didn't want to be looked at funny or have any kind of special treatment. My doctor told me that this pain on contact would continue to be a problem as long as I had the plates in. Once my arm was strong enough, the plates could be removed.

It was six months later, early in December, when the plates were finally taken out. It was a great Christmas present! The surgery was pretty straightforward; I was in and out of the hospital the same day. I needed a new, final cast for a few more months until the doctors could see from an X-ray that the holes from the screws had filled in with calcium. That would mean my bones were solid and I would no longer need the support of a cast.

My range of motion, strength and dexterity were coming back at a normal rate and this was the last visit to the doctor that I would need for quite a while. It had been a long haul – thirteen months – but it was almost over.

Or so I thought.

He asked me if I had any questions, and I had only one.

I stretched my hand out on the table in front of him.

"When I lay my hand flat like this," I told him, "no matter how hard I try, I can't raise my thumb."

After examination, the doctor told me that at some point the tendon attached to my thumb had snapped, most likely from rubbing against the plate, and I would have to come back immediately for surgery to fix it. They would take a tendon from my index finger – because that finger, for some reason, has two tendons – and they would re-route it so that it connected to my

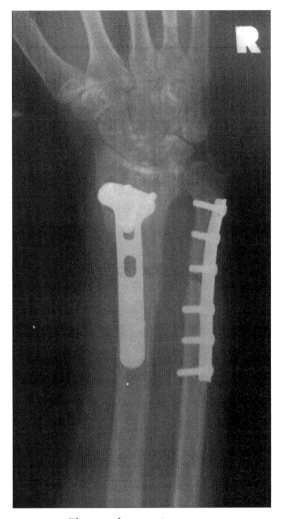

Plates and screws in my arm

thumb. There would be some pain involved and I would need more months of physical therapy.

I said no. I was sick of all of it. What if I didn't have it done? My doctor told me that my thumb would slowly move towards the middle of my hand, causing my hand to eventually be useless.

"I don't care," I replied with the tired frustration of a teenager who'd had enough.

"I'm not going through all of that again."

I looked over at my mother.

"I can't take any more," I told her. "I'll just live with it the way it is."

She looked at me with an expression that blared, "You can't be serious?"

I nodded in confirmation.

"Ya. I'm done."

I was a very determined kid and I preferred to solve my own problems. I guess I was a little hard to handle at times because I wanted to do things my own way. My parents sat me down and explained that although they sympathized with my feelings, there was no way they were going to let their now fifteen-year-old son make a decision to have a ruined hand for the rest of his life.

"You know what, Billy?" my father finally said. "It's not your decision. You're a minor and we are your parents. We love you and we want you to be well. You're gonna have this last surgery. End of story."

Two weeks later, just days before Christmas, I did have the tendon fixed and to my great relief, I healed up fine.

Of course my parents were right when they insisted that I agree to that final surgery. And yet, it wouldn't be long before their admonishing words would replay in my head.

It's not your decision. You are a minor.

In an eerie twist of fate, those same words would surface again soon enough, and would prove to be a pivotal factor in my life – maybe ultimately, in my survival.

TWO

A CLEAN BILL OF HEALTH

BY THE TIME the March winds blew in three months later, I was given a clean bill of health. My doctor told me that I could go back to all of my normal activities, including skateboarding, as long as I wore a wrist brace while I rode. My parents had no issues with me going back on the skateboard; at least not that I was aware of. They knew it was as natural to me as walking.

It was April 4 when my friends and I went to the local skate park, a perfect day with blue skies and bright sun. It was the first time we had all been together in a long while. It felt so good to roll around and my confidence was returning quickly. I had really missed this!

Once I became comfortable moving around the ramps, I started trying some tricks. On my second attempt at jumping over a trash can, I fell on my arm and felt the bone snap in half! It broke just above where the brace ended.

My friends came rushing over as I held my arm in place and announced to them, unbelievably, that I had broken my arm again. I knew my parents would be devastated, but I was more worried about the new pain I was already feeling.

I felt awful about interrupting the skating for my friends. It was such a gorgeous day. I decided I would let them stay awhile and I would just sit and wait in the car. We could go to Boston to see my doctor when they were done.

Shortly thereafter, one of the guys came rolling over to the car window to check on me.

"You okay?" he asked.

"Ya."

"Do you want me to lift your sleeve a little so we can take a look at it?"

"Sure," I offered.

As soon as he touched it though, I realized that was a bad idea.

"Ow! No, don't touch it! That hurts."

"Alright. Sorry." He stepped back.

"C'mon guys," he signaled to the others. "Let's get Billy out of here. We're going to Boston."

"Woo hoo!" they called out as they headed for the car. "Let's go skating in Boston!"

The plan was that we would stop off at my house to let my sister know what had happened before we drove to the city. The car ride home, however, was brutal; the pain was escalating. I told the guys we were going to have to call an ambulance to get me to the doctor.

As soon as we got home and Jenny got a look at me, she ran shrieking from the sight. I felt so sorry that she had to keep witnessing my traumas!

We called the ambulance and when the EMTs came, one of them had to manipulate my arm and my bones. Boy, did that hurt!

The doctors had to put in a new plate and thirteen screws, two more than the last time. This hardware would stay in my arm permanently. (To this day, it often gives me a dull ache. So far it has only triggered one airport scanner to go off.)

Blessedly, my recovery was quicker this time. My doctor told me that if I was careful, I would probably be out of the cast by the end of June, and I would finally be well once more. My twenty months of pain and healing had almost come to a close.

At a young age I had already learned that life could deal some tough blows, but by the time I turned sixteen, I had proven to myself that I was a pretty tough kid. I had survived a serious accident – enduring all of the pain and surgeries – and I decided I was really no worse for the wear! I was feeling great, ready to get on with my life.

I believed the hard times were all behind me.

THREE

SYMPTOMS

IT WAS MEMORIAL Day weekend, 1994, and summer vacation was only a few weeks away. My arm was almost completely healed, and my friends and I were impatiently counting down the days until the school year was over.

My best friend, Scott, was in Boy Scouts, and his dad was one of the troop leaders. Troop #78 was going on a field trip that weekend to Washington, D.C., and they invited me to tag along. Scott and I were psyched! Scott was an avid skateboarder too, and we both knew that D.C. would be a fantastic place to ride.

Over the years, my friends and I had collected a hefty pile of skateboarding magazines, and we had seen plenty of glossy photos of the pros grinding rails and doing flips down the city stairs. As I poured over the pages yet again, I held one up to Scott.

"Look at this," I showed him. "This is awesome! There's marble everywhere. Sidewalks and staircases! We're gonna rule this place!"

Scott gets the troop ready while I "chill" in the shade.

We "high-fived" each other, celebrating our tremendous good fortune. We couldn't wait to get there.

We were in the midst of planning our dream trip when our fantasy came crashing to a halt. We asked Scott's father if we could bring our skateboards, not allowing ourselves to even consider that he might say no.

In typical parent fashion, he squashed our great idea in record time.

"No way," he replied with a shake of his head. "That is not happening. This is not that kind of trip."

He lectured on. "We're going as a group. We're gonna see a lot of beautiful monuments. Experience some history.

"This is our nation's capital, boys. There's gonna be a lot of people around, a lot of tourists. We're gonna be orderly and respectful. I can't have you guys flying and jumping all over the place. The last thing I need is you two crashing into somebody or getting hurt. I can't have you getting into trouble."

"But Dad!" Scott tried to interrupt.

"Sorry." He put up his hand to signal that the conversation was over. "My answer is final. No skateboards."

We were stunned. Our plans were crushed before we had even begun! We groaned and begged – swearing to promises that we would obey and be careful – but it was no use. There was no changing his mind.

We sulked around, not willing to accept this terrible news.

"I can't believe it," said Scott, slamming his bedroom door behind us. "What is he talking about? I'm not going to *crash* into anybody!"

I shook my head in shared disbelief.

"Why does he think we're gonna get in trouble?" Scott continued to rant. "When was the last time we got in trouble?"

"I don't know," I said.

"Well, what are we gonna do? We gotta do something!"

As we sat there together, fuming over the situation, it wasn't long before we decided we weren't going to give up that easily. We started to plan – to scheme – and we knew in our hearts that somehow, some way, those boards were going to Washington, D.C.

On the morning of the trip, we knew the parents would probably give our bags an extra look, so we packed them with great care. I wrapped my clothes around my good skateboard and stuffed it deep into my duffle bag. When we arrived at the bus in the morning, I casually headed towards the group with my bag in one hand and a decoy skateboard in the other. Scott did the same.

The leaders swiftly confiscated our decoy boards and we all loaded onto the bus without a hitch. Our plan was working! With our bags and hidden boards safely stowed under the bus, we made our way to the nation's capital.

Our group spent the first day visiting a lot of the typical tourist spots. President Clinton was in his first term in office. We toured the U.S. Mint, the Capitol Building, and the Vietnam Memorial. The "wall" really quieted us as we walked past its length, trying to digest the magnitude of the thousands and thousands of names inscribed there in memory. We finished off the day eating dinner at the Hard Rock Café where Wolfman Jack was spinning records.

About halfway through the second day, we were allowed to buddy up with a friend and leave the group for a few hours to

"Sliding down a ledge" in a D.C. park

go exploring around the city on our own. I worked it out with the bus driver to let Scott and me stay on the bus until everyone else had left. The driver delivered us a few blocks down the road and as soon as we jumped out, we opened up the luggage hold and dug out our skateboards. No one else from the group saw us or knew we had the boards. We had done it!

To have the chance to skateboard around that amazing city really was a dream come true. Scott and I spent a glorious afternoon riding and searching for spots we had seen in movies and in our magazines, snapping pictures along the way. It was a blast – and we didn't crash into anyone.

The hours flew by, and by the time we happened to look at a clock, we were already twenty minutes late for the bus check-in. We pushed and pushed as fast as we could for five city blocks. We felt the strain on our legs and our lungs as we realized how much longer those blocks were than the neighborhood ones

Doing my tricks in D.C. with my final cast still on my right arm

we were used to back home. I was struggling to keep up and seemed to be having trouble catching my breath.

When we saw the bus on the other side of the park, we somehow managed to ramp up our pace for the final yards. Sweating and apprehensive, we finally reached our group. Not only were we very late, but we had the forbidden skateboards in hand. Unfortunately, when we had devised our original plan to sneak our boards on the trip, we hadn't thought about how we would get them back *on* the bus. There was nowhere to hide them now. We knew we were in a lot of trouble.

Scott's father was furious. "Say goodbye to your skateboards boys. As soon as we get home, I'm tossing them right into the wood chipper."

I was quiet as a mouse, slumped in my seat, the whole trip back. I was ashamed for getting into trouble and having Scott's dad disappointed in me, especially because I had been an invited guest.

There was another reason, though, for my solemn mood during that trip home. Physically, I wasn't feeling very well. My neck was sore and my body ached. I closed my eyes and tried to sleep.

At least I did get my board back when we got home. The long bus ride had softened Scott's father's anger and he unceremoniously returned our skateboards to us.

A couple of days later, I developed a lump on the side of my neck that was very tender. I also couldn't shake a strange feeling of exhaustion.

Normally after school I would ride my skateboard or play soccer. I was a halfback on the Norwell High School soccer team and I spent hours running and practicing every day. Lately, all I wanted to do after school was collapse on the couch. I barely had enough energy or appetite to even finish my supper each night. This was not like me at all.

I didn't mention any of this to my mother; I was a quiet kid and I usually kept my problems to myself. I figured there was no sense in getting her all worked up about me.

My parents hadn't noticed the lump yet. I almost always had a "hoodie" sweatshirt on, so my neck was frequently hidden from view. My parents hadn't had the opportunity to witness my lack of energy yet either. I hoped whatever was causing all of this would just go away.

It didn't.

In fact, it did the opposite. The lump kept growing, and one day in school I was not feeling well at all. I went to see the school nurse. She took a look at me and gave my mother a call. She made us promise to get it checked; she had recently seen a similar lump on another kid and it had turned out to be serious. We told her that I had a physical scheduled for an upcoming summer program, so we would be sure to have my doctor take a look at it.

As fate would have it, on the day of my doctor's appointment, the lump and soreness were gone and I felt fine. At the end of my exam, the doctor said that everything checked out okay and he asked if I had any questions. Remembering my promise to the school nurse, I mentioned the tender lump that had been on the side of my neck.

He felt around the area but found nothing. He thought that maybe the symptoms had been from a recent cold I'd had. I was relieved when he said it was probably nothing to worry about. He did tell me to keep an eye on it and if the lump came back, to call him.

Two days later I woke up with a sore neck again and reached up to find the lump had returned. I showed it to my mom as I was getting ready for school, and she immediately got on the phone to call the doctor. They gave us an appointment for that same day right after school. I already wasn't feeling well and I didn't want to do anything after school but come home and go to sleep.

That afternoon at the doctor's office, after a battery of tests including for mono, strep, tuberculosis, and even parasites, nothing appeared to be wrong. They sent me down one level to the X-ray department where they took pictures of my neck and chest. When they were done, they told us the doctor would call us the next day with the results.

My mother went back upstairs to the office to pay for the appointment, and I went to wait in the car. I didn't know it at the time, but when my mother went back to pay, she happened to notice the X-ray technicians in a side room looking over my pictures. Seeing the looks on their faces, she knew.

Something was very wrong.

Shortly after supper the next day, I was lying on the couch watching *Night Court* on TV when the phone rang. My mother picked it up and it was the doctor. As soon as she finished speaking with him, she hung up and paused briefly before calling me into the kitchen.

"Billy? Come here a minute."

"What?" I asked with some hesitation. "Was that the doctor? What'd he say?"

The doctor had said he still didn't know for sure what was wrong with me, and I was going to have to go to a specialist in Boston to have more tests done.

"Mom! More tests?" I complained. "Why can't they just figure it out? I don't wanna go."

She replied with a sigh. "Apparently they need another test, Billy. I'm sorry, honey. You want to find out what it is, don't you? So we can take care of it? So you can feel better?

"You need to get your energy back, right? So you can get back to soccer? And get rid of this?" She reached over to look at the lump.

The doctor told her that from what he saw on the X-ray, he believed I had something called Hodgkin's Lymphoma, but he could not confirm this without further tests. If it turned out that's what I had, he said it was easily treatable.

They would need to perform a biopsy of the lump in my neck.

I had no idea what Hodgkin's Lymphoma was. My mother knew, but she didn't let on to me. She kept her voice calm and even.

"Sweetie, don't worry about it. We'll get the test done and we'll figure it all out. Okay?

"Go to bed now. We'll talk about it in the morning."

"Ya. Okay," I reluctantly replied.

She gave away no sign of her emotion as she hugged me good night.

My parents used to beam when they told me I was the son they always wanted. They proudly proclaimed the day of my arrival to be "Billy Day," and from then on it was an event to be cherished and celebrated.

I remember my mother explaining, "When you adopt a son, I believe it might be even more sacred than having a naturally-born child. You have to *wait* for him, and *pray* that he will come to you. When he does, it's like no other gift in the world."

I was her beloved son and now I was in real danger. She went down to the basement to find my dad. She started to cry and told him that the doctors thought I had cancer.

"What? What are you talking about?" He stared at her, disbelieving. "They told you that?"

"Ya. They think it's Hodgkin's Lymphoma," she nodded through her tears. "He'll have to have treatments for cancer." My dad stood there, stunned, as my mother continued.

"They said they can treat it. They have to do the biopsy first. To find out. To be sure. Oh my Lord. My boy. My little boy. What am I gonna do?"

My father didn't know what to say, what to do. It was such a shock. He was just watching her, listening, trying to grasp what she was telling him.

When she had told him everything she knew, he held her and tried to comfort her.

"Okay, take it easy. Let's just take it easy," he said. "It's gonna be alright. It *has* to be alright. Let's not get ahead of ourselves, okay?"

She nodded, wanting so badly for it to be alright.

"We don't know for sure yet, right?" he said. "Maybe they're wrong. Let's just go one step at a time. Okay?" He took a deep breath as he tried to take it all in.

As my mother nodded, my dad felt his heart sink. He shook his head, thinking to himself, it *can't* be cancer. It just *can't* be.

As I said, I had no idea what Hodgkin's Lymphoma was, but I had already proven over the last couple of years that I was tough. So, I decided – whatever it was – I would handle it. I would just get the biopsy done and go from there. Plus, they had said it was easily treatable, so it couldn't be that bad.

Or could it?

FOUR

AUNT JUDY

SCHOOL WAS FINALLY out for the summer and my mind should have been on planning some hang time with my friends, working on my skateboarding tricks, and generally just enjoying a couple of relaxing months – maybe even getting a summer job. Unfortunately the reality was that I had to have a lump biopsy. This was really lousy timing.

The drive up to Boston was one I had become all too familiar with over the last couple of years. On our way to get the procedure done, my mother and I passed Children's Hospital and parked at the building next door.

As we pulled into the lot, I looked up and read aloud the words "Dana Farber Cancer Institute." I asked my mother why we were there. She didn't answer me.

She seemed distracted; I knew she was concerned about me, but it seemed like there was something else on her mind, too. I assumed she didn't hear me, so I let it go. At the reception desk, I saw a sign that read, "Jimmy Fund Clinic."

I asked her again, "Why are we here? I thought that the Jimmy Fund was for kids with cancer?"

That's when she told me that Hodgkin's Lymphoma was actually a form of cancer. I wanted to lie down and give up right there. Cancer? I had not even considered such a horrible possibility. At sixteen, I thought I had faced the hard times already and survived.

Then I started thinking about my Aunt Judy and I felt a shiver of fear go through me.

Aunt Judy and Uncle Joe had a cottage on Mousam Lake in Shapleigh, Maine. During the summer, they would invite the whole family up to stay for a weekend or longer. It was a real treat for all of us, being on the lake. We could go water skiing, fishing, take boat rides or just sit on the dock and soak up the sun.

Sadly, one year there was a malfunction with the furnace and the entire cottage burned to the ground. Luckily no one was hurt, but everything was lost. Only the dock – resting over the water – survived the fire. The whole family got together and rebuilt the entire cottage. I think some of the guys enjoyed spending their vacation time building the house more than they would have just sitting on the dock. It made everyone feel good to be able to help.

When the cottage was done it looked great, even better than it did before. It was bigger now, which was good because after doing all that work, we wanted to spend as much time as possible up there in the summer.

I don't remember whose idea it was to pull that old dock out of the water and use it as a bar, but it was a great one. Everyone carved their names and funny sayings into the top of it. After that it was covered with a thick coat of polyurethane to preserve it forever.

Aunt Judy

To celebrate the house being finished, everyone who had helped with the re-build came up for the weekend for a big party. I was thirteen years old and spent most of the night playing darts while the adults had drinks and danced around. This was the first time I had heard the song *Shout*, made famous in the late '70s by the movie *Animal House*. When the song came on, everyone sang along and danced to the music. Aunt Judy was up on the bar, hamming it up ... "a little bit softer now...a little bit louder now." It was a joyful time and a wonderful weekend for all of us.

Aunt Judy was a breast cancer survivor. When she was first diagnosed, her doctors told her that the cancer was only in her breast. They removed her breast and were confident that they had cut out all of the cancer cells.

A few years later, shortly after the house party for the new cottage, Aunt Judy found out that her cancer had returned. This time, though, it was in her liver and was spreading rapidly. The doctors said that because the cancer was growing so quickly, normal chemotherapy wouldn't be effective.

The lake house after the rebuild

She agreed to receive experimentally high doses, and the treatments made her very, very sick. They also offered her marijuana for the debilitating pain she was suffering, but she decided that that just wasn't for her, so she never used it.

Around this same time, her family and friends threw her a "surprise" birthday party. It wasn't really a surprise though; she knew about it. When they asked her what she wanted for her birthday, she said her only wish was to still be around to come to the party. She made it.

In the beginning, when Aunt Judy had her breast cancer diagnosis, the doctors told her that they saw this kind of cancer all the time and it was easily treatable.

So there I was, standing at the reception counter at Dana Farber – with my mother announcing to me that I possibly had cancer. The doctor said that what I probably had would be easily treatable. Weren't those the same words that Aunt Judy's doctors had told her years before?

"Was I going to be sick like that, too?" I wondered. "With a treatment that would be just as bad – or worse – than the disease?"

Being the kind of kid I was, I didn't say anything else about this to my mother; I kept my feelings to myself. In the back of my mind, though, I was already working on a plan.

Just in case.

FIVE

THE DIAGNOSIS

THE ONCOLOGIST EXPLAINED the biopsy procedure to us. They would remove the lumps, which were actually swollen lymph nodes, and test them at their lab. Before he could discuss any treatment options, he would have to confirm the results of the biopsy. He walked us over to Children's Hospital where they would put me under anesthesia to perform the test.

As we walked through the halls, my mother and I passed by a lot of children, most with their hair gone and none of them looking too well. Seeing them, she was worrying about me and wondering, "My God. What can he be thinking seeing all these sick children?" She knew I didn't usually say much, and I wasn't saying much now.

After the biopsy I was exhausted both mentally and physically. It would take a few days to get the results and all I could do now was go home and wait. I didn't know what to think. What if this was serious and I was really sick? What if I was dying? I just wanted to go home and go to sleep. Maybe then I would wake up and this whole thing would be nothing more than a horrible nightmare.

We got home and I was surprised to see my sister there. She was supposed to be at camp. She and my dad were sitting on the couch and I could tell they had been crying. I assumed it was because they were worried about me. It tore me up to see them so sad on my account.

I went over to them and told them not to cry, that I'd be okay. This time, however, it wasn't about me.

"Your Aunt Judy died, Billy," my dad said sadly.

She had actually died the day before, and my parents hadn't told me a thing. Not one word. I was stunned. We all knew how sick Aunt Judy had been, but we had always held out hope.

My dad explained to me that when they got the call, he and my mother decided that he would go up to camp in the morning and get Jenny. My mom would take me to Boston for the biopsy as planned; since it was already scheduled, they didn't want to put it off. I tried to absorb all that they were telling me, but it was a shock that all of this had gone on without me even knowing.

Aunt Judy's wake was hard. I don't think Uncle Joe knew yet that I might have cancer when he started telling me how awful the chemo was, and how sick it had made his wife. He said it was heartbreaking to watch her go through the treatments; it was like a poison that burned her up from the inside.

"She always tried to keep a brave face for the family, you know?" he said to me.

"But when no one was looking, I could tell. I could see that she was in a lot of pain. She was a real trooper."

As I listened, I tried not to look scared, but I shuddered to think that maybe the next funeral would be mine.

We came home from the wake and there was a message on our answering machine from my oncologist. My whole family stood around listening together. My results were positive.

Positive! I officially had cancer. I couldn't believe it. We were all devastated. None of us even knew what to say.

What was going to happen to me? My normal life, whatever future I had envisioned for myself – that was all in question now. I feared both the known – and the unknown.

I couldn't help it, but my next thought was, "Start chemo, get even more sick, and then die anyway. First Aunt Judy and now me." Her experience really frightened me and I didn't want to go through that toxic treatment. I started to reason that if I am dying, I'd rather just die from the cancer than suffer like she did.

Whatever the solution, if there even was one, it wasn't a pretty picture. My future looked bleak.

SIX

TESTS

NOT LONG AFTER that fateful call, it was time for a routine check-up on my arm to see how it had progressed since my accident. The doctor who had performed my surgery seemed uneasy. He had heard about my cancer diagnosis and wanted to assure us that the work he had done on my arm had in no way contributed to the development of my cancer.

Why would it, I wondered? Could the stress from my accident and the surgeries have somehow caused my cancer? My oncologist had told us that my cancer was mostly genetic. This gave my mother and me something to ask about when we met with him later that week to discuss my treatment options.

I needed to relax and think about things, so I went down to the supermarket to skate around. After awhile, my mind was still racing and I needed more of a distraction. I went into the store to buy a Mountain Dew and to thumb through the latest *Thrasher* skateboard magazine.

A kid from school saw me and came over to say hi. He could tell something was up and when he asked me what was wrong, I shared the news about my cancer diagnosis.

"Wow, man. That's awful," he said.

"Ya."

His eyes lit up then as he told me about his mother's experience with breast cancer.

"Hey, my mother had cancer and she used this alternative medicine from Canada," he said. "She's fine now. You should look into it."

"Oh, ya?" I replied, absently flipping through my magazine.

"Ya, I bet your doctors don't even know about it," he continued on. "She gave herself these shots."

I was only half listening. I thanked him and I left. After that, I decided not to tell any of my friends I had cancer. The whole thing just tired me out. I didn't want to talk about it – and yet, months later I would appreciate how meaningful that conversation had been.

Hodgkin's is a cancer that begins in the white blood cells and spreads from lymph to lymph. There are four stages to the disease. Oncologists claim that stages 1 and 2 have a 90-95% success rate if treated with a combination of chemo and radiation. I had yet to find out what stage I was at, but testing started right away.

I really didn't know what to expect, what to prepare for. Being only sixteen, I just had to go along, do what was asked, look to my parents for guidance, and hope that it would all be over with soon. And pray. I was going to be intimately familiar (again!) with doctors, hospitals, tests, and discomfort. But this time it wasn't just a broken arm. This was cancer. This was serious.

The first test I had was a CT or CAT scan. The night before the test I had to drink some kind of dye – they call it "contrast" – that would help the machine see the insides of my body. I was told to mix it with Tang to help it taste better. Well, no matter how much Tang I added, it tasted awful, so I just tried to get it over with and drank it as quickly as I could.

The next day during the scans, I had to stay completely still with my hands over my head and an IV in my arm. I had to hold the position for a half hour at a time. Somehow I even fell asleep during one session.

The second test, called a Gallium scan, was a lot more scary for me because the test required that I have radioactive particles injected into my bloodstream. They told me the radioactivity of the tracer would diminish over a period of days or weeks, but just knowing that I had this foreign substance in my body, whose name began with the word "radioactive," made me very uneasy.

After the injection into my arm, they sent me home for a few days while the radioactive gallium citrate tracer traveled around my body, building up in my body's tissues. As the particles moved through me, they would then light up the cancer cells. When I returned to the hospital, I had to lie down on a table while a camera circled my body for three hours. The end result was a three dimensional picture of my insides.

By the third test I was becoming comfortable enough with everything going on that I started asking all the technicians and nurses about what they were doing. I thought, who knows?

After all this time in hospitals, maybe I would be a doctor someday. But today I was a cancer patient who was about to have a full body X-ray.

I had to lie on a table again, but this time was given a lead blanket to put around my waist to protect my genitals from the radiation. The technician went into the control room and spoke to me through an intercom. I started thinking about all the X-rays I had had because of my accident.

I was concerned about it, so I asked her, "How much radiation is bad for you?

"I've had a lot of X-rays over the last couple of years, and the other day they *injected* me with something radioactive."

"Don't worry about the radiation," she said. "When we do our tests, the radiation only goes where we want it to go.

"There's a very small field where we take the picture," she continued. "Also, it's not enough radiation to be harmful."

Not satisfied with her answer I asked, "Then why do I have this blanket over my stuff, and why are you telling me this from behind a lead wall?" I don't recall her answering me.

The results of my tests showed that I was at stage 2A, which meant it was found in my neck and throat but not below my diaphragm. My treatment plan had three parts.

The first thing my oncologist wanted to do was remove my spleen. Even though there was no cancer detected there, he wanted to be safe. Next, I would go through six months of chemotherapy and finally radiation. He wanted me to start immediately.

I didn't say much. Deep down I didn't believe that this was going to work. I knew chemotherapy was toxic. I was thinking to myself, "We don't put poison into a well body, so why would I want to put it into a sick body?"

The other thing bothering me was, if this treatment does work for my cancer, what do I have to look forward to down the line? Will the damage cause the cancer to just reappear somewhere else? I kept wondering how I could get out of this, but my doctor wasn't offering me any other solution.

He explained the basics of how the chemo would be administered. The first step would be to insert a central line into my body above my heart. A central line is a plastic reservoir with a long tube which is placed under the skin. The tube runs up to the collar bone and then travels back down to the aorta. Apparently this is an efficient way for the nurses to inject the chemo.

I was to receive treatments once every two weeks – every other Friday. We were given a list of possible side effects of the kind of chemotherapy I would be receiving. The name of it was ABVD which is short for the names of the drugs it is made of: Adriamycin, Bleomycin, Vinblastine, Dacarbazine. The side effects of these drugs included such possibilities as loss of appetite, hair loss, susceptibility to infection, bruising and bleeding, skin problems, sterility – and the list continued on. It was sickening to read.

As my doctor wrapped up his explanation, I realized that this was it. I was headed for the dreaded chemo and there wasn't anything I could do about it. Before starting my regimen, my parents would have to sign a release form saying that they understood all of the risks involved.

I went from scared to terrified.

So, the doctor wanted to remove my spleen. The spleen is part of the lymphatic system and Hodgkin's is known to spread there, as well as to the liver, bone marrow and other organs. Even though my spleen showed no sign of cancer, the doctor felt that removing it would be wise.

Without my spleen, however, I would need to take antibiotics for the next couple of years, and I would be more susceptible to catching colds and other infections.

This made no sense to me. I was against it. I told him that since they hadn't found any cancer there, I was choosing to keep it. Thankfully, my parents supported me on this.

After much discussion, he ultimately agreed and I kept my spleen. With this first decision I made about treating my cancer, I had already begun my long journey of advocating for my own health.

The doctor wanted me to start the chemo right away. As I said, the timing on this couldn't have been worse. I really wanted to enjoy at least some of my summer vacation like other normal kids, and I needed to prepare myself mentally for the ordeal ahead.

He gave me a two-week reprieve before I had to begin.

SEVEN

CHEMOTHERAPY

MY TWO WEEKS went by too quickly. It was hard for me to enjoy the start of summer knowing what was to come. I went skateboarding whenever I could, which always made me feel better. I still didn't tell even my closest friends that I had cancer. I was sick of people trying to be careful around me. After my accident with the truck and all of those surgeries, everyone at school had made a point to steer clear of me in the halls, thinking I was fragile. I didn't want to be fragile.

A couple of days before I was to have my first chemotherapy treatment, we met with my oncologist at Dana Farber and he explained what he was about to do. Remembering our conversation with my arm surgeon, my mom asked if there were factors besides genetic disposition that could have caused me to get cancer. We also wondered if there were foods I should stay away from, or if taking vitamins could help me to become healthier.

My oncologist told us that vitamins and diet have no effect on cancer. He said if your child has cancer, a good way to raise his spirits is to let him eat whatever he wants. If a burger and fries makes him happy, go ahead and give it to him. They even had a McDonald's, a Pizza Hut and an ice cream shop attached to the hospital. My doctor's answer was disheartening to me, the fact that there was nothing I could try besides chemotherapy to get well. I sure didn't want to start it, but if that's all he was offering, what could I do?

On the day we returned to the hospital for the first treatment, it was time for my parents to sign the waiver which would release the hospital from any liability from the potentially debilitating side effects. They really struggled to sign it. The long list read like a horror story: nausea and sickness, red urine, flu-like symptoms, weight gain, weight loss, mouth sores, hair loss, constipation, altered sensation, heart damage, change in pigmentation, damage to the lungs, damage to the veins, increased risk of blood clots, sore eyes, and loss of nails.

I didn't have to wait for the drug to cause me nausea. Just reading that list was making me ill.

Another possible side effect was secondary tumors. In other words, the treatment I was going to use for my cancer might give me more cancer. I didn't want it at all. Poison to make me better? And for what? To live through this laundry list of side effects only to develop another cancer? I know I was young at the time, but it made no sense to me. Even though we were at one of the best cancer institutes in the world, I just wanted to get out of there.

It was then that the issue of my being a minor reared its head once again.

I looked up from where I was sitting, and I said to my parents, "I really don't wanna do this."

"I know, Billy," my dad replied softly.

"No, I mean it," I said. "Like, I *really* don't wanna do this. Like, let's just leave and go home. We'll figure out some other way."

"Listen to me." My father sat down beside me. "There *is* no other way. Okay? If there was another way, these doctors would tell us."

"If I was eighteen, I could just walk out of here." It was an irrelevant threat, but one I still wanted to make.

"Ya, well you're not eighteen," he replied, with an exasperated look.

"Your mother and I love you. We want you to be well, so we're gonna have to do this." My dad was firm.

"Here, Sue." He passed the papers to my mother to sign.

I knew my parents thought they were looking after my best interests when they told me that I had no choice. They didn't want to lose their only son.

There would be no getting out of it. I was trapped.

I was sent to surgery to have the central line put in. The plastic tube that went into my heart had a bubble on one end, just underneath my skin. Once the tube was in place, while I was still under anesthesia, they injected my first dose.

I awoke feeling groggy from the anesthesia and had a strange metallic taste in my mouth. I also had a three inch cut on my chest with a big bump under it. Surprisingly, I didn't feel as bad as I had expected. I had survived my first dose! I allowed myself to relax a little. Maybe I would be one of the lucky ones. Maybe I would get through this without the horrible side effects I feared.

Two weeks later it was time for my second dose. When I got to the hospital, one of the first things they did was clean the central line in my chest with a saline solution. As soon as they started that saline flush, my head would get light and I could taste the salt. I learned that if the line wasn't cleaned on a regular basis, a blood clot could form. This was potentially dangerous because if the blood clot broke away, it could get stuck in my veins and kill me. Great.

The chemo treatments were administered in a good-sized room with a TV in the middle, in case any of us wanted to watch. There were probably twelve other kids in there. As I looked around the room, they didn't look good to me. I really didn't want to be like that. I just kept to myself, noticing how sick and weak they looked.

A nurse came into the room and wheeled a full tray of syringes over to my bedside. Some were as large as 70 cc. This nurse wasn't friendly at all. She didn't even speak to me. She put on rubber gloves and stuck a needle that was attached to a clear plastic bag full of dark orange liquid into my central line. As it flowed into my body, I immediately began to feel sick. It tasted like rust in my mouth and it made my jaw hurt. The whole process was overwhelming.

When the first bag was empty, she put on a second pair of gloves before picking up the next bag. As I've said, I was normally a quiet kid – not much of a communicator – but I wondered why she had done this, so I decided to ask her.

"Well," she replied, without looking up from her chore, "I need these in case the medicine leaks out of that central line. It's very strong and would burn a hole through my skin."

I couldn't believe what she was telling me. Tears started to well up in my eyes, but I managed to ask her, "And you are putting this right into my heart?"

She seemed unfazed by the question, and apparently didn't feel that a response was necessary. I lay on the bed and looked out the window. I could see people walking around outside – normal, healthy-looking people. I wanted to be one of them.

They kept pumping fluid into me which meant a lot of bathroom visits. My urine was dark orange and had a foul odor. Wherever I walked, I had to drag around an IV hitched to a pole. I had my mother there with me the whole day but I didn't talk to her much. I felt like a prisoner, a person with no control, who had been captured as part of a big toxic experiment. I tried to keep my eyes closed as much as possible.

It wasn't long after the next dose before my hair started to fall out. My family and I went to Myrtle Beach, South Carolina to accompany my dad on a business trip. We took one of my friends with us too. At the same time, my sister was about to start college, so we stopped at Liberty University in Lynchburg, Virginia to move her into her dorm room. The whole trip took about nine days, and towards the end of it I noticed that I was starting to lose my hair. By the time we got home, it was coming out by the handful.

The next morning while I showered, the accumulating hair on the stall floor was causing the water in the drain to back up around my feet. I couldn't stand losing my hair this way. I was so upset, so mad at the reality of what was happening to me. I got out of the shower and went to get my dad.

"Let's just get this over with," I despaired. "Shave my head."

During those first few weeks of treatment, as soon as the initial side effects wore off, I would head out to the backyard to my ramp. I would skate for hours, running through my repertoire of different jumps and grinds. The familiar sound of my skateboard wheels riding and clapping against the wood kept my mind focused as I glided back and forth across the length. It calmed me and gave me a temporary salvation, taking my mind off of my troubles.

As soon as I stepped off the ramp, the distraction was gone and I was back facing the reality of my cancer.

Every other Friday I would go into the hospital in the morning and wouldn't get back home until 5:00 p.m. Soon after that, I would head over to my friend, Scott's house to lie on his couch and watch TV. After each treatment, I would spend two days being sick before I started to feel better again. Mainly my symptoms were fatigue, nausea, a burning metallic taste in my mouth, a sore jaw, and foul smelling urine. I also felt emotionally drained. I started wondering how long I would last before I died.

After my third and fourth doses, it was taking me longer and longer to recover. On the day of my fourth treatment, the nurse admitted to me that I had lost about 15 pounds. I noticed at the hospital that some of the other kids who usually got their chemo the same time I did weren't there. I wondered why and then I just assumed they were probably too sick to get any more.

When summer ended and school was back in session, I was excited because soccer double sessions were starting up. I had played for a number of years and I loved it. I was hoping to be picked for the varsity team.

I barely made it through the first day of practice. As a halfback, I had a large area of the field to cover, which meant constant running. I was crushed when I realized that I was too weak to keep up.

My coach used to call me "Hollywood" because I always wore a pair of sunglasses to practice. As soon as we finished for the afternoon, I reluctantly walked over to him to tell him my devastating news. I wouldn't be able to play. I broke down in tears in front of him, telling him about my cancer. He was so sorry. He wished me the best and told me to come back and re-join the team as soon as I could – that there would always be a place for me.

By my fifth dose I had lost twenty pounds and was feeling worse and worse each day. My parents had to call the school to let them know that my many absences would continue.

I went in to have a CAT scan done to find out if the treatments were working. The results showed that the tumors were shrinking. It was working. The problem was I felt like the chemo was killing me at the same time. After watching my aunt die from chemo, I just figured the same thing would happen to me and that I would probably only survive another five or six months.

I decided I wouldn't do another dose, that I would rather enjoy the rest of my life, however short it might be, than be sick from these treatments. I was not going to go back to the hospital.

Of course I knew my parents would never agree to this, so I had only one option – the emergency plan I had started to hatch months before.

I would run away.

EIGHT

RUNAWAY

I WENT OUT back to the place where I did my best thinking – my ramp – and jumped on my board to skate for a while. I had to plan my next move and there wasn't much time. I decided my only chance was to leave home immediately before my next scheduled chemo treatment. There would be a few days then when the side effects of the previous dose would have finally subsided. It would be during that small window of opportunity that I would feel strong enough to travel.

I set my sights on California. When I was a young child, I lived there with my family for a few years, and I had fond memories of that warm, sunny life. It was there that I first learned how to skateboard, and it was also where I built my first one, using a piece of pine and the discarded wheels of my sister's old roller skates.

I pictured myself living quietly on a long stretch of sandy beach where I would fall asleep to a beautiful sunset and never wake up. It would be a tranquil and peaceful way to go – as opposed to spending my final days in a hospital, plugged in to a cold tangle of tubes and machines. There was no way I was doing that.

I felt tremendous sadness to be leaving my family and friends, to never see them again, but I wasn't afraid to die. My mind was made up.

I didn't have any money, so I started calculating in my head the sources I could think of to make some quick cash. I would need bus fare and enough food to last me at least a few months. I had a savings bond stashed in my dresser drawer that my grandfather had given me. I had a lot of skateboard parts I could sell to my friends, and videos and baseball cards that I hoped they'd want to buy. My extra pair of soccer shoes would also be an easy sell. My plan was coming together and it seemed doable.

By the time I sold my meager belongings, I had a sum of just over three hundred dollars. My friends never questioned why I was selling my stuff. They were just happy to add to their own collections.

A week and a half after my fifth treatment, I had my bag packed – some clothes, my Walkman, and my skateboard – and was feeling well enough.

It was a few days before Halloween and I went with my school on a field trip to the John F. Kennedy Library in Boston. Throughout the day I was even more quiet than usual, knowing that I would soon be leaving my classmates and would never see any of them again.

We learned about all of the great things JFK had done with his life, and I was sad that I would not have the same chance to pursue my own dreams, to make my own mark on the world. I thought about just leaving the group and running away then and there, but I didn't have my money with me – and I didn't have my board.

The next day it was late afternoon, and the sun was beginning its descent. My mom was getting ready for church, and my dad would meet her there later; he was finishing up some work in his basement office. Jenny was away at school.

Normally I would have gone to church with my mother, but today when she asked me, I told her I was not feeling well. I watched as her car pulled away from the house, and I felt the emotion wash over me as I realized this was going to be the last time I saw or spoke to anyone in my family. I loved them all and I hated to leave them this way.

I looked around at my room one last time, and although I did my best to shrug them off, persistent tears stung my eyes in defiance. I brushed them away; this was no time to cave. It was now or never, and I was going.

I had written a goodbye note earlier that day, explaining to my parents why I had to leave. I took the folded page out of my pocket and carefully smoothed out the creases as I left it on the shelf in my room.

It would be my last communication home.

Dear Mom and Dad,

By the time you read this note I will be gone. The reason I left is because I could not stand going to the hospital anymore. I feel like the medicine is killing me instead of curing me. This is not a last-minute decision. I have wanted to leave ever since I was diagnosed. I wish I could do this without hurting you. Please forgive me. I love you all very much. I am in God's hands now.

Love always, Billy

Minutes after my mother left, I was on the phone to my friend, Craig. He was a skateboarding buddy, and he was the only one I knew with a car. I knew I could depend on him to give me a ride without asking too many questions. After a couple of rings he answered.

"Sure, I'll give you a ride," he said. "Wherever you want, as long as you're buying gas. I'll pick you up in twenty minutes."

I couldn't believe it was almost time to leave. I would have Craig drop me off at the local train and I would head to South Station in Boston to buy my bus ticket. It would be my first time traveling alone, but I assumed it would be easy enough. I would just buy a ticket and go.

I pulled my bag from its hiding spot under my bed, and I slipped out the door to the front yard. My dad never heard me leave.

I didn't have to wait long before Craig's '76 Chevy Nova rolled up in front of me. My friends and I used to pile into the brown sedan to go searching for new places to skate around town. I threw my bag into the back seat and jumped in front for one more ride.

As we drove to the train, I told Craig I was going to visit a friend in Boston to go skateboarding for the weekend. He didn't question my story. I think he was more concerned with getting some gas money than he was with my weekend plans. As he dropped me off at the station, I grabbed my bag and said goodbye.

I was on my own now.

I immediately felt a sense of relief, knowing I would not be suffering any more chemo, but almost as suddenly, I felt a chill of fear that my parents or the police might already be looking for me, to bring me back home...and to the hospital.

After a short train ride, I arrived at South Station and made my way over to the Greyhound bus ticket counter. I didn't know exactly how I was going to get to California, but I had started looking at maps when I was planning my escape and I had decided to take a southern route. Since I would be sleeping outside, I figured I might as well travel where the weather was warm.

On one map I had located a lake town in Louisiana and it sounded like a peaceful place – a place where I could camp, hunt and fish for food. As a child, I had learned how to fish at Aunt Judy's lake house in Maine, and I had also practiced some with a bow and arrow. I imagined that I knew enough about the outdoors to find food and shelter for myself.

Louisiana sounded like the ideal place to rest before continuing on to California. I went to the ticket counter and paid for my fare. I jumped on the next bus heading south. The bus was nearly empty, and I chose a seat towards the back where I sat looking over the details of my itinerary. The first two stops were New York City and Washington, D.C.

The bus shifted into gear and we were on our way. Once on the road, I watched the familiar stretch of highway pass by and I bid farewell to my home and my friends. It wasn't until we were an hour out of Boston that I began to relax. I stopped looking over my shoulder to see if the police or my parents were on my trail. No one was coming. I had made it!

I was nervous and excited at the same time. No more doctors or hospitals. It was such a relief. I was free! I only hoped that the note I had written would be enough to explain to my parents why I had left. I felt very badly about running away, but I was desperate. I believed I had no other option. I hoped they would forgive me.

It was near midnight when the bus pulled into Grand Central Station in New York City. I got off the bus and I was pretty apprehensive. Everyone around me seemed to know where they were headed; I wasn't really sure what to do next.

Since it was my first time in New York, I decided to take a brief look around. I had an hour before my next bus left for D.C. I ventured out of the station to take a walk. Even though it was late at night, there were people coming and going in all directions. Neon signs were lit up as far as my eye could see and hustling taxi cabs crowded the streets.

I walked a few blocks and a woman appeared, coming towards me wearing sky-high heels, fishnet stockings and a mini-skirt. I tried not to stare but I could not take my eyes off of her. As I passed by her, she spoke to me.

"Hey honey."

I didn't know what to do, so I politely gave her a nod to acknowledge her greeting and kept walking. I heard the "clack clack" of her footsteps stop and turn around to follow me.

"Hey hun, hold on!" she was calling out as I walked faster to get away from her. "You want a date for tonight?"

I was about to start running when I saw a little grocery store. I ducked in the door and peered out the window, my heart racing, to make sure the woman did not follow me. With relief, I realized she was gone.

I mulled around the store for a few minutes looking for something to eat. I paid for a gallon of water and a loaf of bread and headed back to the bus station. I got in line and waited for the next bus. It had been a long day and I was tired and ready to get some sleep.

While I had been receiving the chemo treatments, I would always fall asleep as soon as I got into the car to return home; the car's motion would be enough to knock me out. As soon as the bus was underway, it was having that same effect on me. I was out like a light for the rest of the night.

I awoke in the morning to the sound of the bus braking for breakfast. I still had my bread, so I split from the rest of the travelers and decided to go for a skate. The driver had announced that the bus would be leaving in a half hour. I gave myself just under fifteen minutes to skate off down the road before turning back.

Anytime I had a layover of thirty minutes or more, I would keep to this same routine. I didn't want to arouse suspicion, so instead of wandering around at each stop, looking like I was lost, I made myself look busy and tried not to make eye contact with anyone. I would store my bag in a locker and go out searching for places to skate.

When I had to change busses in major cities, like D.C., Philadelphia, and Atlanta, the layover time was anywhere from one to four hours. That gave me an opportunity to spend a good amount of time outdoors and breathe some fresh air.

I realized I had to watch my spending. By the time I had reached Washington, D.C., I had given seven dollars to the poor and only spent two dollars on myself for the bread and water. After that, I stopped giving money to people who asked me for it. I had to look out for myself.

After two days riding the bus, I was getting close to Louisiana and the lake. I closed my eyes for a moment and imagined how it would look. The sun would be shining across the water and the large, old trees hanging over the banks would provide comforting shade. I would catch fish and build a simple shelter. Whatever supplies I needed, I would walk to town to buy. I thought I had it all figured out.

When I finally stepped off the bus, my muscles were tired and ready to stretch. The destination was unfortunately nothing like what I had imagined. The bus station was at a truck stop with a small diner next door. There was no lake anywhere in sight.

I was pretty hungry, so I walked over to the diner to order some breakfast. As soon as I went in, I briefly surveyed the simple layout of the place and sat down at one of the empty tables near a window. When I had finished my food and paid the waitress, I grabbed my bag and went outside in search of the lake.

I walked down the road a ways and came upon a small neighborhood. The air was hot and I had broken a sweat. After only twenty minutes carrying my stuff through the humid Louisiana heat, I needed to find a place to rest. The neighborhood looked like it led to a wooded area. I wondered if maybe the lake was hidden on the other side.

I started walking toward the modest homes but I didn't have a good feeling. As I went deeper down the road, I saw that the houses were little more than shacks with bars covering their windows. The ones lucky enough to have been outfitted with air conditioners had chained them to the window bars. Everything looked dirty.

I was really sweating and needed to get into the shade. I saw a bridge up ahead and I made a beeline for it. Getting out from under the sun was a relief, but immediately something didn't smell right. As I looked around, I realized in horror that I must have stumbled upon the neighborhood pet cemetery – except that none were buried.

Without looking back, I got out of there fast and retraced my steps to the bus station. I approached the counter and asked the clerk if there were any campsites nearby for the lake. She raised an eyebrow at me.

"This is a truck-stop town, honey." She gave me a quizzical look. "I don't know too many people come here to camp."

Upon hearing that, and after considering my unsettling visit to the nearby neighborhood, I felt I needed to come up with a new plan. If I couldn't camp by the lake, I might as well keep on riding the bus.

"How much is it to Houston?" I asked her.

"Twenty dollars," she replied, as she tried to size me up, waiting for my decision.

The last skateboard video I had watched at home had a segment dedicated to popular spots in downtown Houston. I had watched the video so many times, I felt as though I already knew my way around the city.

"Okay," I said, as I pulled my money out. "I'll take one, please. One-way."

I tried to look confident, as if this was not a set-back for me at all. I took the ticket and went to sit and wait for the bus.

The station was empty except for me, one other man, and the few clerks behind the counter. With nothing else to do, we all sat back and stared out the front window at the big rigs refueling their tanks.

Our silence was shattered when a young woman banged through the front door, wild-eyed, swinging her bags.

"Lock the doors! My old man is comin.' He's right behind me!" she yelled out.

"Who's comin'?" one of the clerks answered back, switching her gaze from the trucks beyond to this sudden interruption, not sure if she should fall for this rude outburst.

"My *old man*! He's gonna kill me," she shook her head knowingly.

"And he will, too! I gotta get outta here. When's the next bus? I need a ticket. Right now!" She was talking and walking at the same time, as she hurried to the counter, dropping her bags and fumbling for her cash.

"I'm not kidding," she warned. "You'd better get the door!"

Before she could even finish her sentence, a car came careening up to the lot and a man came charging out of the driver's seat. We all began to pay attention with new interest. One of the employees, making the quick decision to believe this threat, managed to beat the intruder to the entrance with her key. She locked the door, and joined the other workers and the woman as they ducked into the back room to call the police.

The angry man reached for the front door handle, and realizing the door was locked, pumped his fist on the glass. He looked at me and the other traveler, commanding us to let him in. I shrugged my shoulders, trying to explain through the thick pane that we were only waiting for the bus, that we had no keys to open the door.

"They're calling the police," I managed to say, as I gestured in the direction of the back room. He cursed loudly and kicked at the dirt. He gave us one last look and threatened to come back with his gun before he turned and retreated to his car. As suddenly as he had appeared, he was gone.

Not long after that, the next bus arrived and the other man and I boarded, along with the still distraught woman. As we settled into our seats, we saw out the windows that a police car had arrived and was pulling up in front of the diner. It was probably just as well that I was out of there, too.

As we drove away from the stop, I felt sorry for the woman and I considered striking up a conversation with her. Ultimately I decided to mind my own business, just in case the boyfriend had a notion to follow us to Texas.

NINE

A FRANTIC SEARCH

I LEFT HOME on October 26, 1994. All the while I was riding buses and traveling from city to city, I had no way to know what my parents were going through. When my dad met up with my mother at church that night, he looked around and asked her casually, "Where's Billy?"

 She looked at him oddly.

"He's at home, isn't he?" she replied. "He said he didn't feel well and didn't want to come."

My dad shook his head. "No. He wasn't at home. I came up from the basement, but I didn't see him there."

My mother shrugged, but didn't think that much about it. My father, however, had an strange sense that something wasn't right.

After church, he arrived home ahead of my mother, and he was frantic when he found my note. He immediately called the Norwell police to report that I was missing. When my mother came through the door, she was stunned by the news.

"We were shocked, horrified, devastated, and helpless," she later lamented to her friends. "We had no idea that Billy felt so strongly against the treatments he had been receiving."

As the reality of the situation started to sink in, my parents were alarmed realizing that I wouldn't be getting any healthcare at all. They knew I would be well for a while. My mother figured I was probably feeling great, being away from the chemo, but she knew that eventually the cancer would grow again. If I came down with a cold or a virus, I wouldn't be able to shake it off.

They were also worried about my safety, a teenage boy traveling alone to some unknown destination. It's a good thing I didn't know it, but their hearts were breaking.

It didn't take them long to realize that once they had reported me to the police, and the police had added me to their missing children's database, there wasn't much else the police could do. My parents were stunned by this fact and would not accept that the search for me would end there. They decided to start reaching out to people on their own.

Early on, the main thing they wanted desperately to know was that I was alright. Oh, if I would just call! As the hours turned to days, they prayed that I would contact a friend or my sister – anyone to let them know I was okay.

I didn't call.

They met with the principal and students at Norwell High School to try to get some clues about where I might have gone. I hadn't told any of my friends about my plans, so they really had no information to share. In hindsight, some of the kids started realizing there had been some hints that I was up to something, especially because I had started selling my belongings. Someone had also overheard me at school asking about bus tickets.

Not long after I was diagnosed, I had written to a friend in California who I knew from when we lived there years ago. I asked her if I could maybe stay with her if I came out that way. I didn't tell her I had cancer. Even though I didn't have any serious plans to leave home when I wrote her the letter, I guess I was trying to lay the groundwork – just in case.

She wrote back to me, and my parents found her reply in my room saying that, sure, I could stay with her. My parents remembered how happy I had been in California; I loved the warm weather there.

They immediately notified the San Diego police.

Days went by, still without any word from me, and the wait was agonizing. My parents realized they were going to have to think of something drastic if they were going to have any hope of finding me.

It was then that my mom turned to my dad and said, "We should get the media involved."

Her decision to do that changed my life – almost as much as the cancer did.

The story traveled like wildfire. Front page articles about me, which included my freshman yearbook photo and phone numbers for the local police and the National Center for Missing Children, were printed in newspapers all across the country.

Lisa Bul, *The Patriot Ledger*

My parents at home, holding up my photo during an interview with *The Patriot Ledger*, November 3, 1994.

My parents started getting inundated with calls from all kinds of well-wishers, cancer patients, and cancer survivors; everybody wanted to help. My parents had to resort to an answering service to handle the volume of calls. South Shore Answering Service of Pembroke, Massachusetts generously donated all the phone lines and staff to field the calls around the clock.

There were up to a hundred calls a day. Television talk show hosts and newspaper editors around the country joined the fray, calling up in hopes of getting their "exclusive" piece of the story. A quote in our local paper, *The Patriot Ledger*, from a staff member at the answering service read: "You don't even know how busy it's been. Just today we had Sally Jesse Raphael. On Friday it was Maury Povitch. *The New York Times*. *The Washington Post*. Minnesota. Arizona. It's wild."[1]

Slowly, a few clues started to drift in. A bus driver reported that he saw a boy of my description boarding a Greyhound bus to New York. In trying to follow my path, my parents found out that tracking someone traveling by bus was almost impossible. There was no system for following a rider, ticket by ticket. They tried to figure out what all the stops were in and out of New York – a daunting task – and they called the police in some of those communities. Police were then checking buses in those locations looking for any sign of me.

Shortly after I reached Louisiana, someone from there called my parents. He had seen my story on *NBC Nightly News*, and he was "pretty sure" he had ridden on the same bus with me.

My parents were documenting every call, every lead on a huge map that they had tacked up on the kitchen wall. They kept track of the clues with different colored highlighters in a desperate attempt to pinpoint my whereabouts. Meanwhile, they kept their vigil next to the phone, always praying I would call.

During this frantic search, my parents were straining to tap every possible source of help, and there were unexpected roadblocks compounding their stress. My dad complained in frustration to reporters at *The Patriot Ledger*.

"Everything shuts down over the weekend, whether someone has run away or not. It drives you crazy.

"If you want to run away, do it on the weekend."[2]

TEN

HOUSTON

WHEN I ARRIVED at the downtown Houston Greyhound terminal, I got off the bus and walked through the station with my skateboard strapped to my duffle bag. I thought back to how scared I had been, doing the same thing in New York City just two days before, and then how I had quickly regrouped when my Louisiana plans had fallen through. I was becoming comfortable traveling on my own, and was pretty proud of my progress so far. I was ready to explore my new home in the "Lone Star State."

I stashed my bag in a coin locker, grabbed my skateboard and headed outside. The sun had already gone down and I immediately felt relief that it wasn't as hot as Louisiana.

As I began skating around the city, my logic led me to look for other skateboarders who might be able to help me find a place to stay. I had learned about a popular skateboarding spot – Jones Plaza – from a video I had at home, so I asked around and headed in that direction.

After an hour or so, I came upon four guys who looked like they were about my age. I approached them and struck up a conversation. I introduced myself as Billy from Boston. Pat, who appeared to be the leader of the group, introduced himself, followed by Chris, Marshall, and Kush.

I told them that I had run away because of family problems and planned on sleeping under the ramps at the Skate Park of Houston.

"Oh ya?" They laughed, glancing at each other with knowing looks. "Good luck with that."

Apparently, there was already a homeless guy living there and, according to them, if he saw me making attempts to move in, he would swiftly boot me out.

Kush spoke up next.

"What about the clubhouse?" he said to his friends. "We could let him stay there?"

"Ya." "Yup." "Ya, sure." They shrugged in agreement, eyeing me for any signs of trouble, and then acknowledging Kush with the all-clear.

"My family owns a strip mall," Kush explained to me. "It's near his house." He pointed to Pat.

"We made a clubhouse there," he continued, "You can stay there if you want. You could bring your stuff over later."

"We're usually all there on the weekends anyway," he added.

"Ya, that'd be great! Thanks," I replied.

"Do I have to pay you or anything?" I looked at the four of them.

"No," Pat shook his head. "No charge," he nodded with a half smile.

Even though I had appeared out of nowhere from another city – another state – being a skateboarder was enough to make

Marshall, Kush, and Pat, where I met them in downtown Houston.

me one of them; we were all connected as loyal members of the same "brotherhood."

"Well," I thought to myself with relief. "That didn't take long. I've already got a place to stay!"

We skated the benches for a while, showing off our tricks and abilities to each other, until a security guard kicked us out. We moved on from spot to spot, skating for the next couple of hours until it was time to make our way to the mall. The guys followed me to the bus station so I could retrieve my bag, and from there we headed over to the clubhouse.

As I walked in the door of the warehouse, all I saw was a huge wall of boxes and crates – nothing that looked like a clubhouse – and for a brief moment, I wondered what I was getting into. Before I had a chance to have any second thoughts, however, they showed me that hidden behind a few boxes was an opening to a space that harbored a couch, a table and candles, with graffiti covering the walls. The guys had been hanging out there for some time and were pretty sure no one else knew about it. They thought I would be safe.

I told them the place was perfect and I stashed my bag in a corner on the floor. We all left and went down the street to Pat's house; he had invited me to sleep there for my first night.

He told me I didn't have to worry about meeting his parents because they would be asleep, and they would be gone in the morning before we got up. It was Halloween the next night and they would be setting up a haunted house all day. The guys wanted to stay up and watch a movie, but I told them I had to sleep. I was exhausted from being on the bus for so many hours. I curled up on the floor and almost immediately was out cold.

I was the first to wake up in the morning and my stirring woke Pat.

"You can take a shower if you want," he said.

After spending two days on a bus, I was definitely looking forward to a shower. I washed up, and I found the boys in the kitchen eating sandwiches.

"Do you eat these up in Boston, Billy?" Pat handed me a sandwich of avocado slices in between two pieces of buttered white toast.

"No, but this is delicious," I told him, "I have never heard of anyone eating an avocado this way. We eat guacamole."

At this point it had been a couple of months since my dad had shaved my head. My hair was growing back, but it was still thinner than normal. I took my hat off and Pat suggested he could give me a

Just hangin' in Houston

better looking cut with a hair buzzer he had. He set me up in the backyard and gave me a fresh new haircut.

I was feeling great. I was showered, had a new haircut, and food to eat – and I had made some friends.

During the time I stayed at the clubhouse, I would read and do crossword puzzles all day until my friends got out of school. I wouldn't go outside for fear of being picked up for skipping.

As soon as school let out each day, I would go over to Pat's house and use his shower. Then we would meet up with the rest of the guys and go out skateboarding. I felt better than I had in a long time.

It was Halloween and we were going to help Pat's parents with the haunted house. First Kush and Marshall wanted to stop off at their houses to shower and change. Chris had other plans, so he went home. The rest of us went to Marshall's house where we watched movies all afternoon until it was time to go.

We skated over to the haunted house around 7:00 p.m. I met Pat's parents and was introduced as a friend who had just moved into the area. The haunted house was mostly done, so we didn't have to help. We headed right for the buffet to fill up on chicken wings and hamburgers. After we ate, we grabbed our skateboards and headed out.

Pat had a friend who was working at a restaurant in the mall and his shift was over at 10:30 p.m. The guy had promised us a bootleg copy of an album we wanted; we had to find something to do for two hours. Marshall came up with the idea of going from house to house asking for canned goods for charity so I would have something to eat at the clubhouse. Between the four of us, we collected enough candy and canned goods to last a whole month.

We bagged up our booty and headed to the mall to wait for Pat's friend. We planned on killing time by walking around the stores, but they had already closed for the night. I needed to use a bathroom, so we walked around the concourse until we found one.

When I came out, the guys were leaning into a big fountain, filling their pockets with change. They told me to "hurry up and get some," so I rolled up my sleeves and joined in. It only took me five minutes to fill my pockets with quarters and dimes. Just then Marshall spotted a security guard coming towards us and yelled "Run!"

I thought we would get away because we had a good head start for the exit, and the safety of the woods was just across the parking lot. However, the faster I ran, the more my pants fell down from the weight of the change. That was when I started tossing handfuls of coins out of my pockets to lighten my load, but we were cut off by two patrol cars. They brought us back to the security office.

I couldn't believe my bad luck! There I was, trying to keep a low profile, and the last place I wanted to be was in front of *any* kind of law enforcement. We sat there as the guard yelled at us for making him run. He complained that he had flat feet and running was his least favorite thing to do. He demanded that we each tell him our names and where we lived.

When he got to me, I told him my name was Bobby and I was visiting from Boston. After yelling at us for about ten minutes for stealing money that was supposed to go to charity, he banned us from the mall for life and let us go. I breathed a sigh of relief when we got out of there.

Once we escaped the clutches of the guard, we headed over to find Pat's friend. After the guys introduced me, he unveiled his pirated copies of Nirvana's album, *MTV Unplugged in New York,* that was set to be released the next morning. We were psyched about this illicit prize, so we anted up our money. We played that album more times than you could ever count.

I was feeling very settled-in in Texas. The people I had met were friendly and welcoming; I was comfortable there. I had quickly fallen into a daily routine that suited me and I wasn't thinking about leaving any time soon. The drama of my running away had faded, and I was thoroughly enjoying all of the experiences in my new life.

In my wildest dreams, I couldn't have anticipated what happened next.

I had been in Houston about a week, and we were in front of Pat's house getting ready to go skateboarding downtown. Pat went inside to tell his dad that we were leaving and a minute later, he came bursting through the front door. "Billy's on TV! Come inside!" We all ran into the house and were *shocked* to see home videos of me on the screen. My mother was there too, crying "Billy, come home."

It was November 4 and the show was *A Current Affair* hosted by Maury Povitch. Maury was reporting all about how I had run away and how my parents had started a nationwide police search for me. When my freshman yearbook picture flashed across the screen, Pat's dad, who had been half asleep on the couch, gave the TV a scrutinizing glance.

"Hey, don't you guys know that kid?" he asked.

I had already turned and quietly made my way outside before he had a chance to get a better look at me. I pulled my hat down and the hood of my sweatshirt tight to hide my face. The guys came running out to join me. None of us could believe what we had just seen on television.

"What is goin' on?" They looked at me with disbelief. "What are you doin' on TV?"

"C'mon. Let's just get outta here. I'll explain everything," I said, as I started walking away.

We hurried to a corner bus stop.

As we rode the bus, I worried to myself, "What if someone else around here saw the show? What if Pat's dad figured it out and called the police?" I shook my head at the thought of it. That feeling of being followed and the fear of going back to the hospital came rushing back to me, completely ruining my happy, carefree mood.

The bus brought us downtown where we found the closest McDonald's and went inside. As we sat there eating burgers, I admitted to the guys the real reason I had run away. They asked me about my cancer and how I was feeling. I told them what it was like getting chemo and losing my hair. They seemed okay with it, and they said I could still stay at the clubhouse – *as long as I didn't die there.*

The more we talked, the more I realized the trouble I had caused and I knew I had to call home. I finished up my food, ran outside to the pay phone, and dialed my number. My body was shaking and my heart was pounding. What was going on? Why was my picture on the TV? Why was I so different from the thousands of other kids who run away? I felt like everyone was watching me.

Mom picked up on the first ring. My father jumped on the line next. They were so relieved to hear from me. They were both talking at once.

"Oh my Lord, we've been worried sick! Where are you? Are you okay? How are you eating? Where are you staying?" My mother peppered me with questions.

"Oh, thank God. Thank God." Just to hear from me was enough for her for the immediate moment.

She then pleaded with me to come home, but I told her I couldn't. I was only calling to let them know I was safe and had people looking after me.

They both kept repeating "Billy, come home! Where are you? Come home right now!"

I told them I was fine but I wasn't ready to come home. I didn't tell them where I was and I asked them to call off the police search. I wanted to stay where I was for a while until I had a chance to figure things out.

As much as they wanted to find me, they also feared that if they dragged me home, I might just leave again. They reluctantly agreed to call off the search, but it was a hard thing for them to do; they were so worried. I told them that I loved them both and that I would call again soon. That was the first of several calls I would make to them over the next few weeks.

Now that I had been on TV and it seemed like the whole country was looking for "the runaway cancer patient," I felt like I had to increase my efforts to stay under the radar. I never wanted to go back to the hospital. I continued wearing my hat down low and I kept on my sunglasses. I did feel I had good cover being with the guys. We all kind of looked the same, with our hooded sweatshirts and our boards. It would have been hard to pick out any individual.

Even so, that night I was pretty scared. I asked the guys if they would stay in the warehouse with me. Everyone told their parents they were staying at Pat's. Pat ran home to tell his parents he was staying at Kush's, and to make sure his dad didn't suspect anything.

We rigged some beds out of boxes of air filters and packing materials and went outside to wait for Pat.

"What are you gonna do next, Billy?" Kush asked me.

I didn't know what to tell him. I liked it here with these guys, but now I was afraid to stay in any one place for too long. If I got back on a Greyhound, I might be identified. All of a sudden, I felt like my options were shrinking.

Pat arrived with a big smile on his face as he pulled a six-pack of beer out of his bag.

"Don't worry about my dad. He doesn't suspect a thing."

We stayed up at the space telling stories and drinking beer. They especially enjoyed my story about getting hit by the truck, and they thought my scars were gross.

Pat finished his beer and grabbed another. "Are you going to die, Billy? On the TV show, your doctor was saying you needed more chemo or you would die."

"We're all going to die, Pat," I replied.

I told them what the chemo had done to my Aunt Judy, and how I didn't want the chemo to kill me. I would rather die from the cancer. The beers were gone and we stayed up telling stories until we fell asleep.

I woke up the next morning to an instant panic. Someone was yelling my name and banging on the door! I woke Marshall up as quietly as possible and told him to get rid of whoever it was. I heard him say to someone that, yes, I was there yesterday, but I had left last night on the bus. It was a girl, and she apparently believed his story and left.

Marshall came back inside and tried to go back to sleep. I was shaking, thinking I was about to get hauled off by the police.

I grabbed him. "Who the hell was that?"

"Chill out. It was just a couple of punk rock chicks looking for you. I got rid of them."

I appreciated Marshall getting rid of the girls, but I wasn't so sure they would stay away. I decided I'd better find a new place to hide. We went to Pat's so I could take a shower and pack some food. Pat told me he had a friend who could be trusted; I might be able to stay there for a couple of nights.

When we returned to the space, the door was wide open and there were cans of soda and a bag of burgers. I turned around and saw what had to be the punk rock girls from earlier walking towards us. I should have turned and run, but these girls didn't look like much of a threat.

As they came closer, they told me not to run; they wanted to help me hide. Their names were Heather and DeeDee. Right away I was stirred by Heather's appearance. I had never seen a girl who looked or dressed like her. She had bleached blond hair, a nose ring, bright green tights, and pink fuzzy slippers. Underneath all of that was the face of an angel.

They had some of the same friends as Pat, and they offered to let me stay at DeeDee's house. Pat agreed it was a good idea to get out of the space for a while in case anyone else came around looking for me, so I told the guys I would see them later and I left with the two girls. Having just met these girls, I was suddenly nervous. What if they were taking me somewhere to turn me in? I decided since they were "friends of friends" of Pat, I would trust them. Plus, I was smitten by Heather's smile.

We arrived at DeeDee's house and I met her mom and her cat. Her mom said not to worry; she was "cool" and wouldn't call the cops. The girls and I went out for some coffee so we could sit down and get to know each other a little better. While sipping our coffee, Heather explained that the reason they felt compelled to find me was because they were both going through illnesses themselves. Heather had diabetes and always forgot to take her insulin. DeeDee had just had a lump removed that her doctors thought was cancer. What a sad little group we were! Daring to laugh at our possible fates, we joked around that we might all be dead by the time we were eighteen.

Later that night we dropped DeeDee off at her house. Heather wanted to hang back and talk to me some more. We went to the all-night pancake house and started making small talk over bottomless cups of coffee. After a few hours Heather became withdrawn, and I was running out of things to say. I kept trying to make conversation, but she was becoming more and more quiet.

"Let's get out of here, Billy."

Once inside the car, she started to open up. She told me that she had a boyfriend – and a baby! Her boyfriend didn't treat her well, and she wanted to get away for a while. She was thinking about leaving her daughter at her mom's and going to San Antonio for a couple of weeks. I told her I could go too, or maybe the two of us could keep going all the way to California. She was overwhelmed with it all and started to cry. I reached over and pulled her into my arms to comfort her.

She began to feel better, but she stayed in my embrace.

"Let's just sleep here tonight and we'll figure it out in the morning," she said.

As she lay against me, I tried to tell myself that I had too many problems of my own to get involved with this girl. She had a child and a boyfriend – even if she didn't like him.

The problem was, I was falling for her.

I hadn't seen the guys in a few days. I was starting to worry that they would be mad at me for spending all of my time with Heather and DeeDee. I felt bad about not seeing them, but I needed to be with Heather. Things had changed.

When I called her the next night, she was crying. "My boyfriend found out we have been seeing each other and he is pissed." He had taken it out on her and promised to hurt me if she and I saw each other again. She kept crying as I tried to comfort her. After several minutes she calmed down, and then I realized she hadn't said a word for about five minutes. When I couldn't get her to respond, I hung up and called DeeDee.

"Hi, DeeDee?"

"Yup."

"Hi. It's Billy. I was just on the phone with Heather, and right in the middle of the conversation, she stopped talking. I don't know why. I couldn't get her to talk. She was crying, and I know she was upset, but I don't think that's it. I think something's wrong."

DeeDee immediately thought that Heather could have had an insulin overdose.

"Oh my God." DeeDee said. "Sometimes if she hasn't been taking care of herself or she's upset, she might give herself too much insulin. She might have blacked out. Oh my God, she could be having a seizure. Hang up! I'll call 911!"

It turned out that DeeDee was right. Heather ended up in the hospital and had to stay overnight to make sure her blood sugar had stabilized. Heather asked me not to visit her because her family would be there and they didn't know anything about us. I was going nuts not being able to see her.

I stayed at DeeDee's for a few more days, trying to keep busy skateboarding to keep my mind off of everything bad that had developed. I started to hang out with DeeDee's friend, Fish – another skateboarder. His parents had heard my story and they assured me they wouldn't turn me in. They offered me a spare bedroom to stay in. I had been sleeping on the floor at DeeDee's, and I couldn't pass up the opportunity to get back to a bed. I moved my stuff into Fish's house.

Fish's mom was home during the day and I became friends with her while everyone else was at school. I felt very comfortable talking with her. I didn't know until years later that she was a counselor by profession. Looking back, I can see why it was so easy for me to open up to her.

Over the next couple of weeks, the story of "a runaway boy" was on the news a lot. My initial plans to continue traveling to California didn't seem like such a plausible idea now that my face was plastered all over the TV. The reporters were still advising anyone who saw a bald teenager with a skateboard on a Greyhound bus to call the police. So I stayed in Houston and tried to blend in with the other kids.

At one point, a guy in Houston called my parents, telling them that his son had skateboarded with a boy fitting my description. The details were accurate, right down to my baseball cap, so my parents were sure it was me.

After I had been gone three weeks, they tried to fly down to Texas to see me. I didn't know anything about it; they didn't tell me they were coming.

To their great despair, the media swarmed Logan airport in Boston, interfering with their plans to travel quietly. They cancelled the whole trip, turned around, and went back home. They were afraid that if the same media attention was staked out in Houston, I might be scared off and run somewhere else.

During those few weeks, I spoke with my parents a handful of times. On one of my calls home, my mom told me to go to a TV and tune in to *CBS Talk Back Live*, a show where callers phone in their opinions on current events. The topic of this episode was "Runaway Cancer Patient: Should he come home and do the rest of his chemo?" Members of the audience and people calling in were giving their opinions about the whole story while my parents were connected to the show by a phone.

I couldn't believe this was happening. My life was on a talk show! Most people who called wanted me to go back on chemo. I knew that they were just trying to help, but they didn't know me. They didn't know what it was like. I didn't want to watch anymore.

I called my parents after the show.

"Billy," my mother said. "You have no idea. There is so much going on here right now because of the story, I haven't even had a chance to tell you most of it." She couldn't contain her excitement and was talking fast.

"People are sending us letters and we're getting phone call after phone call from everyone who has seen the story. Cancer survivors are leaving their phone numbers, Billy, and their beeper numbers for you, inviting you to call them if you want to talk. It's unbelievable."

Then she took on a slightly more serious tone.

"Billy, listen to me. It's about *alternative medicines*. People have taken time out of their day to pick up the phone or pick up a pen and let us know that there might be *alternatives* for you – treatments that the doctors wouldn't know about." She wanted me to come home and read over some of this information.

Then she said if I didn't want to do the chemo, *she wouldn't force me*. That was a pivotal moment. She was giving me an "out."

I promised I would think about this "alternative medicine" and call them again soon.

I told Fish's mom about the phone call and she asked me, "What do you think, Billy? Would you consider going back home if there really were alternatives?"

I had a lot to think about, but I was considering it.

Heather was home from the hospital and I went over to see her. She still didn't feel well and wasn't talking much. I wanted to grab her and scream, "What were you thinking? Things get a little tough and you give up?"

As soon as the words popped into my head, though, I realized I was doing the same thing if I didn't look into the alternative treatments. I decided I owed it to myself and to my family to investigate all of my options.

I told Heather about what my parents were learning from all the calls and the mail, and she lit right up.

"You mean there are other treatments out there that might work? That's awesome!"

"Ya, but if I want to try them, I will have to go home. I don't want to leave you," I told her.

She didn't hesitate with her response. "Go home and get better, Billy."

The next phone call home was a quick one. I said hi to my dad and he asked if I had decided what I was going to do. I hesitated for one moment and he cut in.

"Billy, you've had your fun. Now it's time to come home."

He was right. Just as strongly as I had felt about running away, I knew I had to go home.

So that was it. The very next day I was on a plane back to Boston. My plane ticket was purchased by Andrea Jaeger of the *Kids Stuff Foundation*. Andrea was a professional tennis player who started the foundation to grant wishes for children with terminal diseases. She had seen the story and offered to help in any way she could to get me home.

When I eventually spoke with her, she also asked me if there was something special I wanted, like a stereo, or maybe there was a famous person I wanted to meet. I really didn't need a stereo, but I told her that there was someone I wanted to call.

There was a professional skateboarder who I idolized. One of his many abilities was his "switch stance," being able to do tricks both left- and right-handed. He was also often wearing casts in his photo ops, which I could certainly identify with. Thanks to Andrea, my wish was granted and I was able to "meet" him on the phone.

I didn't even have a chance to say goodbye to all the guys – only to Pat. I hugged him and thanked him for everything they had done. He promised to say goodbye to the others for me. DeeDee and Heather came with me to the airport. We were all sad to part ways, but we knew it was the right decision. We kissed and embraced and wished each other the best, promising to stay in touch.

The police at home told my parents that I should use an alias when purchasing the airline ticket to help keep the media from finding out I was coming home. My parents had already sacrificed too much about their personal lives to the news reports, and they wanted my homecoming to be private. So, for the flight home, I was Mr. William Turner, a name my parents came up with for me.

As my plane taxied down the runway preparing for take-off, I took a deep breath and reflected on the events of the last four weeks. I had managed to make it all the way to Houston, and I had met good people who helped me and kept me safe. I believe that God was watching over me.

Now, however, just in case His plan was to have me die in a plane crash, I pulled out the journal that I had been keeping since I left home and made my last entry. I wrote that I wanted all of my savings to be donated for research to the hospital that treated my Aunt Judy. (I still had about seventy-five dollars left.) I wanted to help end this epidemic, and at the time, that was the only way I knew how.

I settled back into my seat and relaxed for the flight back to Boston. I had no idea what was waiting for me when I returned home.

ELEVEN

MEDIA BLITZ

MY PLANE MADE its final approach to Logan Airport. It was a cold, raw, rainy day just before Thanksgiving. As we touched down, I was surprised to feel my heart pounding as I anticipated seeing my parents. After what I had put them through for the last month, I wasn't sure exactly how much trouble I was in. I was afraid that as soon as they saw me and realized I was alright, their relief might quickly turn to anger.

As the other passengers began exiting the plane, I waved them by, letting them all get off ahead of me. I took a few deep breaths and then stood up, grabbed my bag, and headed for the door.

I stepped off the plane and saw my parents across the tarmac waiting with a state trooper. A second officer was making his way over to me. I had been told that the police would be there on my arrival to escort us, but seeing them almost made me feel like I was about to be arrested.

As I walked from the airplane, I could see the open doorway to the airport building behind my parents, and I caught a glimpse of people crowding the entranceway. I saw a flash of cameras. I knew my parents had done a couple of interviews, but what was that about? I still hadn't grasped the magnitude of the media attention that my story had generated.

My parents and I hugged, and they took a good look at me until they were satisfied that I was okay. There wasn't time, however, for a lengthy reunion. The trooper immediately ushered us to his car so we could make a quick getaway. He dropped us off on the opposite side of the airport where my parents' car was inconspicuously parked.

Once the three of us were alone and on our way, my parents began to fill me in on all of the events of the past month. They were, of course, happy to have me back home, but at the same time, they were more than a little annoyed with me for running away and they were stressed out from the media. Even though it had worked, inviting the media in had caused them a great loss of privacy. They repeatedly tried to impress upon me how much commotion my running away had created.

On our way out of the city, we got hung up in the Boston "Big Dig" gridlock – the most expensive highway project in the U.S. (and the most badly managed) – and the trip that should have taken an hour turned into about two and a half. Between trying to keep up with everything my parents were telling me, and having to sit impatiently in the crawling traffic jam, it was a very long ride home.

I was not prepared for what was awaiting us on our front lawn. It was a media circus of grand proportions. Trucks from every TV station were parked in front of our house.

As we approached and I looked out the car window, I was beginning to understand why my parents had been advised to use an alias to buy my plane ticket. It didn't, however, appear to have helped much, as I witnessed the frenzy in front of me.

My dad watches the media staked out on our front lawn.

What I really wanted right then was some quiet time to unpack and relax, but that was not possible with reporters constantly ringing the doorbell. I suggested to my parents that I might be better off hiding out for a couple of days at my friend, Alex's house, and they agreed. I re-packed my bag and without even time to spend the night in my own bed, I left home once more.

My friends starting calling the house and wanted to see me. We met up at one of our favorite skating spots, an abandoned CVS, but we were followed everywhere by reporters trying to take our pictures and get interviews. I just wanted to hang out with my friends, and I didn't have anything to say anyway.

I expected things would settle down after a few days, but every time I went back home, I'd have to rush into my house to avoid the crush of questions and cameras. It was a crazy time. From then on, there was no privacy for the Best family.

One evening when my friends came by the house, they pulled up around back and a cameraman with a bright light tried to follow them inside. This made me feel very violated; I was angry. On the one hand, the media had helped me to come home, and I appreciated that, but on the other hand, this was a hard time for my family and we needed our privacy.

One of my friends went outside and attempted to get rid of the cameraman by grabbing his lens. We also joked around with the idea of turning the garden hose on them. We weren't serious; we were just trying to keep a good sense of humor about the whole thing.

We all jumped into my friend, Craig's Nova and sped away in hopes of losing a particularly persistent reporter. We drove around town for the next twenty minutes trying to lose the guy. We finally parked at the high school and ran indoors where we hoped he would not follow. We skated around, cruising the empty hallways and enjoying the echoing sound of our wheels against the smooth floors.

As soon as we decided the coast was clear, we exited the school and headed for the car. The reporter was right there waiting for us! We were ambushed with camera lights. We jumped into the Nova, but not before the cameraman got his front page shot. The picture was of Craig in the driver's seat with a cigarette hanging out of his mouth. Craig was not allowed to smoke and he got into a lot of trouble because of that picture.

After the story appeared on the front page of the local paper, *People Magazine* called and wanted to do an interview. They did a two-page spread on me and titled it "Road Warrior." Their graphic was a huge photo of me on my board, airborne in the middle of a jump in my backyard. It was very cool.

I was also receiving random items in the mail and offers from people across the country who had seen me on TV. Some were inviting me to visit them, offering to fly me out to where they lived. Girls were sending me their photos, asking me to send them one of mine. Because of my stay in Houston, the *Journeys* store in Texas sent me a supply of clothing and all kinds of shoes to wear.

I didn't pay attention to most of it, but one guy who was involved with celebrities – mainly musicians – asked me if I wanted an autographed picture of anyone famous. I told him I was a Jethro Tull fan, so he sent me a signed photo of Ian Anderson playing the flute.

The offers that had anything to do with skateboarding were the ones that caught my eye the most. There was a guy who was a skateboard enthusiast as well as a well-known contemporary graphic designer. He happened to see my interview in *People Magazine* and he decided to give me a call – just to offer his support to a fellow skateboarder and to send me his best wishes.

He had created this great "Andre the Giant Has a Posse" sticker campaign in 1989, and he sent me a huge supply of them; I had fun slapping those up all over town.

Next it was *Good Morning America* who called and they offered to fly my family to New York City so we could be guests on their show. They said I could bring a friend, so I invited my friend Tom.

It's funny how quickly things turn around. Barely a month ago I had been in New York City, a timid kid on the run, and now I felt like I was the talk of the town. The limo dropped us off at the Rihga Royal Hotel New York, which was palatial compared to anything I had ever seen. Our rooms were on the 50th floor and overlooked Central Park. My parents had a room on one side of the hallway, and Tom's and mine was on the other.

We had the day to explore the city and go to a show; the network had provided us with some complimentary tickets. Mom and Dad went sightseeing and to the Broadway musical,

Cats. Tom and I had tickets to sit in the audience of the *Late Show with David Letterman.* We had a couple of hours to kill beforehand, so we charged around the streets, jumping off stairs and grinding benches.

We skated as long as we could, and then it was time for Letterman. We arrived right on time to see a long, snaking line out the door and around the corner. I had been told our names would be on some sort of list, so we skated past everybody to the front of the line and showed our IDs.

"Hurry up. The show's about to start." The security people ushered us through the door.

Our seats were about ten rows back, right in the middle and we had a clear view of the whole stage. The guests on the show that day were comedian Pauly Shore, actress Meryl Streep, and musical guest Duran Duran featuring Grandmaster Flash.

The show was not one of the funniest ones I had ever seen, but who could complain when you were watching it live? My favorite part was when Duran Duran played their hit song, *White Lines.*

As soon as the group stepped out on stage, a few people in the audience to my immediate left began yelling and screaming at the top of their lungs.

After they quieted some, I turned to one man and said, "You must really like Duran Duran."

He pointed to the guitar player with pride. "That's my nephew!" he boasted.

We gave each other high fives and watched the rest of the performance, clapping and cheering.

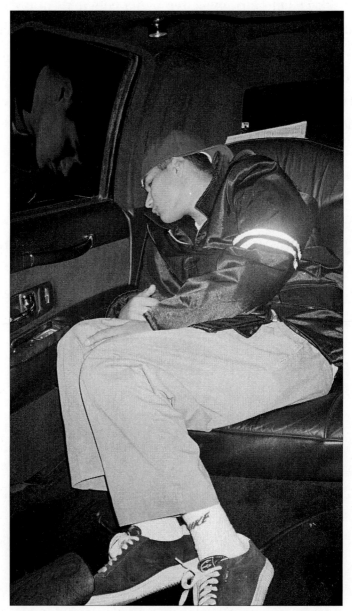

Trying to sleep in the limo

After the show, Tom and I stayed out skating until midnight. It was much better riding after hours when the stores were closed and there were fewer people walking around. When we finally returned to our hotel, we had to drag ourselves down the hallway. We were exhausted from all the skating we had done. Neither of us had fallen too badly, but seven hours of pushing yourself around on a skateboard can take its toll on your body. I did not hesitate to take advantage of what the room had to offer. I hopped into the Jacuzzi tub and ordered room service from one of the three phones in the bathroom.

After my luxurious soak, we turned on the TV and sat down in front of our food. We didn't linger very long in the room, however. We decided it would be more fun to eat on the roof, so we mustered up the energy to relocate. We took the elevator four more floors to the top, climbed a couple flights of stairs, and found an open door. With the vast city of lights canceling out any midnight darkness, the view was endless; it seemed like you could see all of Central Park, Manhattan, and beyond from up there.

After resting and finishing our food, I had an idea and I told Tom I'd be right back. I returned to our room and gathered up every piece of paper I could find there, including the newspaper and the hotel's information directory. Tom didn't know what to make of it when I reappeared and held the pages out in front of him.

"What's all that for?" he asked me.

"How many kinds of paper airplanes do you know how to make?" I asked him, smiling.

He broke into a broad grin.

"Enough," he replied.

We immediately got to work and made every possible design of airplane we could think of. We launched them off the edge of the building – dozens of pieces of paper floating fifty-five stories in the air. It was an awesome sight. Once we had exhausted our supply of aircraft, we sat for a while just enjoying the moment.

I was having a good time overall, but it was a bittersweet experience. Attending the TV shows, seeing the celebrities, and staying at the hotel with all of its perks were certainly great fun, but my reality was that I was there because I had cancer. I could never forget that.

The next day was insanity as soon as we stepped out of the limo in front of the ABC building for the *Good Morning America* show. It was November 28, 1994. We saw famous people everywhere we looked. Security was expecting us and promptly escorted us inside. Dolly Parton was standing there watching our mouths drop and said, "Come on in darlin.' I ain't gonna bite."

We were led down the hall past Miss Parton and told to go upstairs to the Green Room. Along the way, our eyes were wide as we gaped at all of the cool photos and memorabilia adorning the walls. I recognized a woman hurrying towards us and I tried to speak to her. All she said was "No autographs!" as she waved past us. At least I would be able to tell my friends I *almost* spoke to Rosie O'Donnell.

We found the Green Room and sat down to a breakfast of delicious pastries and really good coffee. We were brought in one-by-one for hair and makeup. I thought this was a silly waste of time because I had no hair and I didn't want any makeup.

"It's just to take the shine off, sweetheart," the stylist told me.

I was starting to get nervous. What if I said something stupid or fell out of my chair on live TV? I comforted myself thinking this would be the last interview I would probably have to do, so I just tried to relax and get through it.

The show went great. Charlie Gibson asked my parents and me the basic questions: What was it like being home? Was I afraid of dying? What was I going to do next?

I told him I just didn't know.

After the show, we were invited to sit in the audience during *Live with Regis and Kathie Lee*. We walked next door and found our seats. Being in the audience was a lot more fun than being on the stage.

Prior to the start, Regis Philbin came out to welcome us all and asked us to look at the number on our chair and remember it. With his typical enthusiasm, he explained that during the first commercial break, there would be a raffle and if your seat number was called, you were supposed to jump up and act excited. When he finished his opening monologue, it was time to call the seat number of the lucky member of the audience.

"Now it's time for our lucky seat number!" he called out. "175! Who is sitting in seat number 175?" No one answered. I was 172, and Tom, to my right was 173, which meant my dad had to be 175.

Regis stepped off the stage and advanced down the aisle towards our seats. He pretended to give my dad a hard time and everyone was laughing; Regis was a very entertaining guy. In the end, Dad received a shiny gold bracelet and a year's supply of Sue Bee Honey, which made the embarrassment worth it, I guess.

We watched a few more segments, waiting for the main attraction – the supermodels! Claudia Schiffer, Elle Macpherson and Naomi Campbell had recently opened a restaurant and they were coming on the show to talk about its success. Unfortunately, they were never given the chance.

Regis came out and calmly announced that someone had called in a bomb scare and we all had to evacuate the building. The stage seemed to magically roll out of the way and huge doors that had been hidden behind it opened to give us all an escape to the street. Everyone left the building.

We were in a sea of people out front searching for our limo when the supermodels started making their way through the crowd. You could see them coming, heads above everyone else. Naomi Campbell attempted to climb into a limo just as the driver exclaimed, "Hey, you can't go in there. That's not your limo." Tom and my parents had caught up to me just in time for the driver to motion to us to get in, and to hear him tell the three tall beauties that this limo belonged to "these guys."

We made it out of Rockefeller Center and went back to the hotel to relax for a bit before skating one last time. I was glad the TV interview was over and we would soon be heading home. I really wanted to start sifting through the piles of mail my parents had received to see what the alternative treatments were all about.

I collapsed on the bed and noticed an orange light blinking on the phone. I rolled over, lifted the receiver and pushed the button. A voice from the front desk said they had an important message for me.

It was the television show *A Current Affair*. They saw that I was in the city and they wanted their own interview. When I told them I was all done with that, they pleaded that they would do *anything* for me if I would agree. They just wanted a few minutes.

After careful consideration, I traded a five-minute interview for new skateboards for me and Tom and a limo to the Brooklyn Bridge Banks, a famous skate spot. They also gave me a video camera.

After we left New York and returned home, I was contacted by The Oprah Winfrey Show. She, too, was inviting me to be a guest, but at this point, I had really tired of the publicity surrounding my running away and the whole chemo story. I thanked Ms. Winfrey's staff, but told them I would not be available for any more television interviews. I needed to get to work finding a viable treatment for my cancer.

I had already wasted enough time.

TWELVE

SEARCH FOR A CURE

AFTER THE TRIP it was great to be home again, but we were plunged right back into the local spotlight. The high volume of phone calls persisted. The media seemed to have an insatiable appetite for the story, and there was also a steady flow of well-meaning strangers who wanted to give me their advice and best wishes. I really didn't "get" why so many people were interested in me.

It became overwhelming. To keep our sanity, we let the answering service pick up the calls for a while longer. I never answered the phone.

We decided we would hold a press conference, hoping that would put an end once and for all to the media's questions. We chose the Ramada Inn in Rockland, Massachusetts for the event.

I was too intimidated by the media – and still uncomfortable with the enormous public response to my story – to do any speaking myself. My dad handled the whole thing. He got up in front of all of them, and I couldn't believe how cool he was about it – like he had done it a hundred times. With dozens of cameras flashing, he was calm and direct. He told the crowd that we genuinely appreciated all the help we had received, but the time had come for some privacy – and some closure – so we could work on finding my cure.

After that, they left us alone – for a while anyway.

Since arriving back in Norwell, I was feeling apprehensive about my proximity to Boston and the dreaded hospital. A persistent thought kept nagging at me; in a few months I would be seventeen. In Texas I would be considered an adult. If I returned to Houston, no one could *force* me to undergo medical treatments that I didn't want. Plus I could see my friends again – and Heather.

Going back to Texas was a tempting idea, and I thought about it more than once, but my parents had promised me they would not mention chemo again if I remained home. So far they had kept that promise. I knew I had to keep my end of the bargain with them too, and stay put and search for a better way to treat my cancer – one that we could all live with.

One of the most blessed results of all the news coverage was that we received enough letters from well-wishers to fill five shopping bags. Suddenly, I had an incredible resource of information to sift through. I settled in and started reading.

We had also received a stack of tapes and videos offering all kinds of creative ideas. Mom and Dad were eager to show me some of the stranger treatments they had come across while I was gone – and there were plenty of them.

One relatively conservative suggestion was to use marijuana as a cancer treatment. The woman's note said she was even willing to send me some if I wasn't able to get my own. Another letter was from a beekeeper claiming that one bee sting per day would heal my cancer. He offered to send me cases of bees.

One of the more memorable therapies involved chick peas. This person claimed to have been healed of cancer by cutting the skin above his tumor and inserting a chick pea. The gentleman was kind enough to provide color photos of the procedure. For a long time after opening that letter, I didn't even want to look at a chick pea.

It seemed to me like all of these people were crazy. When my parents told me they had found alternative ways to treat cancer, bee stings, marijuana and chick peas were not what I had envisioned. These people all seemed like quacks.

I was looking for something else – I just didn't know what.

I didn't give up the reading, however, and surprisingly, I started to see a pattern. I began to sort the letters into like piles. The pile that grew the quickest was from people who believed diet had helped them overcome their cancers. Hundreds of letters all shared a common thread – that people suffering from cancer should eliminate four basic food items from their diet. Even though my oncologist had assured me that diet had no effect on cancer, these letters advised which foods I should be eating and which ones I would be smart to avoid.

The first food I was supposed to stop eating was animal protein. Some said an occasional piece of chicken or fish was okay, but absolutely no red meat should be consumed. There were two reasons.

The first was that even though the meat had nutrients, it also required a lot of energy to digest, and that was energy that my sick body needed to conserve – so I could heal. The second reason people gave for avoiding beef was that the growth hormones given to cows pass into us when we eat the flesh; there was a suggestion that the growth hormones might contribute to some cancers.

The next item off the menu was dairy products – because of the fat content. Third was white flour, and fourth was sugar, which is a known inflammatory.

The letters gave me reason to reconsider things that I had always accepted without question. Even though I grew up believing that milk was good for you because it is a source of calcium – and we need calcium for strong bones – some people don't see it that way. Many had written that milk is meant for baby cows and not for humans, mainly because of the fat. I started to question whether it was wise for me to continue drinking it.

Another recommendation that was mentioned repeatedly was a tea – namely Essiac tea. About a third of the letters mentioned this tea as being *a must* for anyone afflicted with cancer. As I read more about this mysterious tea, I learned that it is made from four herbs, and its purpose is to purify the blood and cleanse harmful toxins from the body.

That sounded perfect to me! Herbs from nature used to cleanse the body. That was exactly the kind of thing I was looking for. I was definitely going to find out more about this tea.

Essiac tea was originally pioneered by the Ojibway Indians.[3] It was popularized by Rene M. Caisse, head nurse in the 1920s, at the Sisters of Providence Hospital in Ontario, Canada.

Caisse first learned about the herbal remedy during a routine day at work when she had an opportunity to discuss breast cancer with a patient. The woman had been diagnosed with the affliction thirty years prior while she accompanied her husband on a prospecting trip through the wilderness of Northern Ontario. Alarmed at her symptoms, she and her husband traveled to Toronto, where the doctors performed a biopsy and diagnosed her with advanced breast cancer. Their recommendation was that her breast be removed at once. The woman had recently lost a friend who had died during breast surgery, and the thought of the operation frightened her.

Before committing to a decision, the despairing couple returned to their camp in the woods where they met a very old Indian medicine man. As they told him their sad tale, he shared with them a remedy that he believed would cure her ailment. Because of the loss of her friend – and since she and her husband had no money for the surgery anyway – she opted to try the medicine man's treatment.

He showed her several herbs growing in the area. He instructed her to make a tea from those herbs and to drink it every day. She followed his directions to the letter.

The woman was nearly 80 years old when Caisse met her, and there had been no recurrence of her cancer in thirty years.

Nurse Caisse was intrigued by the story, to say the least. At that time, a cancer diagnosis was as good as a death sentence. Caisse wrote down the names of the herbs, and she decided that if she ever developed cancer herself, she would absolutely try the tea.

As years passed, Caisse encountered more and more cancer patients who had exhausted all treatment options that medical science had to offer them. She remembered the tea, and began to research the herbs and refine the tea to her own specifications, eventually naming the tea using her own surname, spelled backwards.[4]

Caisse decided to begin treating people with the tea, knowing that it would do no harm and could possibly help. Although she was never licensed as a medical doctor, Caisse's work over fifty years is well-documented and includes a long list of testimonials from people who claim to have been helped by Essiac tea.[5]

As I continued reading, I began to think, "All of these people can't be crazy." There were too many similar letters. There had to be some truth to them. I decided to bring this information with me when I met with my doctor.

One night around 11:00 p.m., the phone rang. I hadn't answered the phone in about two weeks, but for some reason without thinking, I reached for it and picked it up. The male voice on the other end asked if I was Billy Best.

I replied warily, "Yes."

He said, "I know a lot of people have been calling you, but I have some information about an alternative therapy that I think may help you."

His name was Richard, and I listened intently as this stranger told me his experience with an alternative therapy called 714X.

Richard was working for a branch of the government when he became sick. He was diagnosed with ALS, Lou Gehrig's Disease. ALS attacks the nerve cells in the brain and the spinal column, causing loss of muscle control leading to paralysis and death. There is no cure. There have been new therapies discovered since then to help slow the progression of the disease, but back in the mid-90s, there was basically no treatment.

"Billy, the only thing they could offer me," he said, "was to monitor the progression of the disease and tell me how much time I had left."

Richard explained how his connections through his work provided him with contacts around the world, so he started searching for something – anything – that would help him. Through his research, he came across an experimental treatment from Canada, which was available to terminal patients through the Canadian Emergency Drug Release Program. The drug was called 714X.

Richard told me that 714X was a solution of camphor, nitrogen, and mineral salts, and it was designed to be injected directly into the lymphatic system. He began using it.

"Before I started the 714X," he said, "I didn't have the strength to walk. I had lost the use of my hands, and my legs were so weak, I had to be pushed around in a wheelchair."

Three months after beginning 714X, Richard was out of his chair, and his hands – although not perfect – had healed enough to open doors and operate his television remote control.

"Billy, this isn't like chemo. 714X works by strengthening your own immune system so your body can heal itself.

"I live close to Canada and if you and your father want to stay at my house, I can introduce you to the inventor and several people who have used it."

Astonished, I took down Richard's name and phone number. After hanging up, I told my mom what I had heard. I told her I wanted to learn more about what this man was talking about and possibly go meet him.

The next day instead of the regular mound of mail, there were only a few letters, plus a plain manila envelope with a New York return address. Opening it up, I found a gray notebook that was about 80+ pages long, entitled *Do No Harm*. After thumbing through a few pages, it started to sound familiar. Wow! The book was all about 714X, the same treatment I had heard about on the phone just the night before.

If there was ever a "sign," I considered this to be one. I showed the notebook to my father right away and told him about my phone call the previous night from the man named Richard. My dad read through the manual twice, and he thought it sounded like it made sense. He was willing for me to give it a try.

It was time for another meeting to talk with my doctors, and my parents and I took information about Essiac tea and 714X with us. We were excited about the therapies and we told the doctors that I was going to try them. I was not going to go back on chemo.

The doctors were respecting my decision to refuse chemo for the moment, but they wanted me to have new tests to see how fast the cancer was growing back. Of course, my parents and I also wanted to know, so I went through the procedures again for both a CAT scan and a Gallium scan.

When my doctor called us with the results, he warned that the tumor had begun to grow around my windpipe. He wanted me to start up a new regimen immediately of six more months of chemo and radiation.

When we said "No, we really want to try some alternative methods first," he asked me and my parents to return to the hospital for another meeting in two days.

Meanwhile, a man named Charles Pixley from Writers and Research, Inc. in New York contacted us. He was the one who had sent me the gray notebook, *Do No Harm*.

Charlie seemed angry and a little radical, but in spite of that, I could tell he wanted to help me get better. He was extremely passionate about his subject. I listened to him intently, and what I gained from our conversation convinced me even more that I wanted to learn about 714X and what it might be able to do for me.

We went to the follow-up meeting with my doctors. When we arrived, we were surprised to see not only my oncologist and radiologist, but also the head of oncology, radiology, psychology, public relations and the head of the hospital!

They were well-prepared with their response to our alternative medicine ideas, and they took turns telling us the different ways I would die if I didn't go back on chemo and radiation right away. They also told me that 714X did not work, and if I gave myself the injections, I would end up piercing my femoral artery and would bleed to death.

I went into that meeting hoping to be able to work with my doctors on my new ideas – to give the alternatives a chance. I was so disappointed by their negative reaction.

Not only were they completely against the treatments, they said they were going to report my parents to the Department of Social Services as unfit parents – as if we didn't already have enough problems! They told us that because I was a minor, they could take me away from my family and force me to do chemo.

As we left the hospital, we were shocked at how badly things had gone.

"They wouldn't really try to take me away from my family, would they?" I wondered in disbelief. I was getting pretty old; I was almost seventeen, and with all the media attention I was getting, I didn't think Dana Farber wanted negative publicity that might make them look like the bad guys.

Luckily – even though it took a few tense weeks – DSS chose not to take action against us. We finally heard that the courts weren't going to pursue the case. It was basically a threat, but thankfully, nothing serious came of it.

We kept a newspaper clipping from the *The Caledonian Record*, of St. Johnsbury, Vermont, which reported that the court charges failed, "largely due to Billy's age and his strong character. The court felt that a young man of 16 who was capable and determined enough to leave home and live on his own... for nearly a month, was mature enough to be the one making decisions about his life."[6]

My parents, however, were really put off by the scare tactics at the hospital. After that, they were even more supportive of my ideas, and they began to believe that there really *might* be other ways to treat my cancer.

We were still being hounded by a number of reporters, so we decided to hold another press conference. This would hopefully get all the remaining questions finally out and answered.

I knew my cancer was growing and there was no time to waste.

THIRTEEN

ALTERNATIVE MEDICINE

IT WAS TIME to get to work on my new treatments. I started my new diet immediately, eliminating the red meat, dairy, white flour and sugar – taking care to follow the advice from the many letters I had received. I also took daily vitamins and supplements, drank filtered water, made food substitutions such as brown rice and whole wheat bread for white, and ate as many organic fruits and vegetables as I could find. My mom started cooking plant-strong meals and brewing up Essiac tea. I was on a mission to put all the nutrients I could into my body.

We switched our soap and household cleaners to natural ones to eliminate chemicals in the house. I even installed a water filter in the shower. The idea was to "clean" my environment of toxins as much as possible to help boost the power of my own immune system.

I felt good following this new regimen because I was taking an active part in my healing process. I accepted Richard's offer to meet the inventor of 714X, as well as some of the survivors who had used it. In our hearts, my parents and I felt it was the right course.

❖

In early January, Dad and I hopped into the Subaru and headed up to Richard's house in Vermont, near the Canadian border. We had dinner with Richard and his wife as they told us everything they knew about 714X and its inventor, Gaston Naessens. We would be meeting Gaston in Quebec in the morning.

We were nervous about what we were about to do. What were we going to say was our reason for visiting Canada? *We are entering your country to get some cancer drugs because they are illegal in our country.*

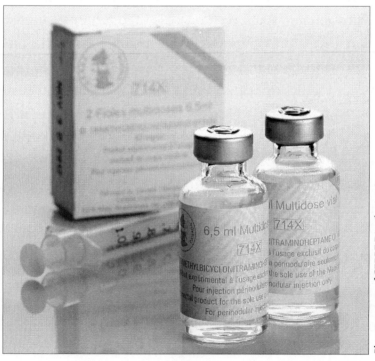

714X

My dad kind of stuttered a little when they asked him why we were going to Canada. I felt like everyone was watching us and that, any minute, they were going to pull us over for looking suspicious. He told the border patrol officer that I was sick and we were going to the big church to pray. We were allowed to pass.

It was only a few miles to Gaston's and we were there in no time. He greeted us at the door with Jacinte, who was his assistant at the time, though years later they would become husband and wife.

Gaston was a French biologist; he did not speak English and we did not speak French, so Jacinte translated everything he said. They welcomed us and showed us around. After we were settled in, Gaston told us he had arranged for some people to be there who could share with me how 714X had helped them.

The cancers they described were all different types and stages, but they were all healed by Gaston's therapy. The thing I remember the most was how this treatment was going to help my body be healthier *without poisoning me at the same time*. After listening to their stories, I was one hundred percent certain I wanted to try the treatment.

Gaston brought us downstairs to his lab where 714X was made. He took one drop of blood from my finger and put it on a slide. He put the slide into his Somatoscope, a powerful microscope that he built. After a few moments, an image appeared on a television screen. We were looking at a video of my live blood at 30,000X magnification.

After a lot of nodding, pointing, and rapid French between Gaston and Jacinte, she began to translate as he described what he saw in my blood. The first thing he told me was exactly what I was looking at. The white rings on the screen were my red blood cells. They did not look good. A healthy red cell is round and has a strong outer membrane. Mine were all crumpled up and stuck to each other. As he pointed to the monitor, he explained that the white blood cells should be moving around like amoebas, cleaning particles out of the blood. Mine were not moving and had bacteria all over them.

The next thing Gaston explained – through Jacinte – were the squiggly lines which he called somatids. Judging by the condition of my blood, and the stage in which Gaston observed my somatids, he thought I could benefit from his therapy.

We made an appointment at a private clinic near Montreal that specialized in teaching people how to self-inject; the staff had been trained by Naessens himself. The clinic had a hospital feel, which made me nervous. I hoped from listening to those who had used 714X that the side effects really would be nothing like chemo. I would soon be finding out for myself.

We met with one of the nurses for a consultation. She told me that she was only there to teach me how to self-inject, not to give me any injections herself. We went to the examination room and she had me lie down. She gave me an ice pack to put on the injection site and told me to keep it there for ten minutes. This was to bring the lymph glands closer to the surface and also to numb my skin.

While we were waiting for the ice to do its job, the nurse told me how to handle the needle and fill it with the liquid. When the ten minutes were up, my skin was sufficiently numbed and it was time for the injection.

I learned to use my femoral artery as a landmark and move four inches towards my navel. The goal was to inject the 714X directly into a lymph node. I was given alcohol to disinfect the area, and I put the needle in.

It was much easier than I expected! The needle was very small, so between its tiny size and the numbing from the ice, the shot didn't hurt me at all. I was so relieved. After that initial try, it took only a few days of practice before I was comfortable injecting myself without supervision.

There was only .1 cc of the medicine to inject, but it had to be administered very slowly. I was really pleased that when it was over, I did not have that awful taste of salty rust left behind like with the chemo. I stood up and was able to walk around without feeling light headed or woozy at all.

The ice pack went back on for another ten minutes after the injection, and while I did that, the nurse instructed me to increase the dosage by .1 cc each day until the fifth day. On the fifth day and each day forward, I would use .5 cc until the 21-day cycle was over. Then I would take a 2-day break and start another cycle. I would keep doing this for the next six months.

We now had a supply of 714X in our possession, and we wanted to take it home with us. We had gone to Canada because that was the only place we could get the treatment. We knew that we *should be* allowed to have it legally shipped to us from outside the U.S., even though it wasn't an FDA approved medicine in our country. After all, it wasn't a narcotic, and it was only for my personal use; I wasn't going to sell it. Still, we were worried. We had heard some stories at the time about packages mysteriously not making it across the border.

Soon enough, we would have to put our faith in having it mailed. We couldn't go running back up to Canada every time I needed my next dose.

Meanwhile, we had it in our hands and we weren't willing to leave it behind. We packed enough 714X to get me through the next twenty days. We tucked it under the seat of the car, with the ice packs and needles, and tried not to look suspect.

The people in Canada and the doctors at Dana Farber *did* agree on one thing. They all counseled me, "We have this medicine, and it can do great things for you, but it can only do half the work. It's going to be your belief and your attitude that will bring you the rest of the way."

I took their words to heart. I did believe in what I was doing. I *wanted* to do it. I was taking an active part in my own healing process, literally giving myself the medicine, and that felt great to me.

We returned home and I was glad to be back, but settling in to a normal routine was going to take a little while. I had to follow my own natural cancer plan and I also had to get back to school, which meant answering questions from curious classmates and teachers. In addition, reporters were still calling to see how the story was turning out. I had to take things one step at a time.

The only thing I cared about was following my treatments and getting my health back.

I started setting my alarm to wake me up an hour earlier than usual. Upon waking I would go to the kitchen to drink my Essiac and get everything I needed for the 714X injections. I played relaxing music and crawled back under my covers with the ice pack on as I prepared the needle.

After a couple of weeks, I felt like a pro and was giving myself the shot without any worry at all. The needle didn't hurt going in, and as long as I remained relaxed and didn't push the medicine too quickly, it did not sting.

After only ten days of my treatment, I was feeling like myself again. My appetite had improved, I was able to make it through the school day without falling asleep, and after school I had enough energy to stay at the skate park until dinner time.

I was getting a lot of attention at school. Kids wanted to know if I was going to die because I had discontinued chemotherapy. I was getting pretty tired of explaining my decisions. And yet, over the next couple of months, my hair was coming back fully, I was gaining weight, and I was looking more and more healthy. I was enjoying being alive, and I think people were starting to realize that *just maybe* I had done the right thing.

We started having the 714X shipped to us, but we had some fear that the FDA might raid our home and take the treatment away. Charlie Pixley, who I mentioned earlier, had once been raided for selling 714X out of his research company. They stormed into his New York office and took all of his files, computers – just about everything.

I certainly wasn't selling it to anyone – and that was obviously a big difference between me and Charlie – but we still couldn't shake a perpetual worry that my stash of 714X would meet the same fate.

My doctors had scheduled follow-up tests for me at Dana Farber for the third week in March to check the status of my cancer.

I was starting to feel some of the old panic returning. "What if the cancer has grown?" I worried. "I just *can't* go back to chemo." I was praying that it would be okay. I knew I was feeling healthy and well, and I hoped that was a good enough sign.

As the date for the tests arrived, I was sweating with anxiety. Unfortunately, the only way to find out about the cancer was to have yet *another* CAT scan and *another* Gallium scan. Back to drinking that awful tasting stuff that I had to put the Tang in. Back to having those radioactive particles injected into my bloodstream.

I didn't want any part of it.

After an excruciating wait, the doctor finally called us with the results. We were almost afraid to answer the phone – talk about a life-changing moment.

I had been through so much already in my young life – surviving my horrible accident with the truck, suffering through all of that pain and trauma; receiving the dreaded cancer diagnosis; running away in desperation from my family and friends; being welcomed back like some kind of celebrity; and finally, defying the norm and searching for an alternative cancer treatment – hoping with every ounce of my being that it would work.

Whatever the doctor's news was, I knew I'd have to deal with it. I gingerly took the receiver, and I couldn't believe what I was hearing.

There was *no evidence of cancer at all*! It was gone!

My parents and I jumped around, kissing and hugging. We cried and laughed. We had done it! I had done it! All of our efforts had worked! It was truly a miracle.

Honestly, I think the doctor was more surprised than I was. I kept repeating, "Really? Really? You're sure? It worked?"

Well...not exactly. He tried to give me a few explanations for why *he* thought my cancer had disappeared. He suggested that maybe it was in "spontaneous remission" or perhaps there was some residual chemo floating around in my system that had somehow managed to shrink the tumor. He even suggested that my cancer had been a "misdiagnosis" – after they had *treated me* for cancer.

The only thing he wouldn't acknowledge was even *the possibility* that my alternative treatments had worked.

So my tumor was gone. My whole family was ecstatic. As I let the news sink in, though, I knew I wanted more. Much more.

The tests at the hospital had been very conclusive at showing evidence of cancer, but they could not tell me if the cancer would *come back*. If there was any way for me to know that, I wanted it.

I learned that the test Gaston did in Canada could pre-diagnose cancer up to two years before you would start showing symptoms. He did this by using what he called "live blood analysis." I wanted to have this test done but we couldn't travel up to Gaston's again so soon. The trip to Canada was a long one, and my father had already taken off too much time from work.

We found out that there were two people in the United States who had been trained to use this particular type of microscope. One was a doctor who lived in California and the other was a dentist – who had been trained by Naessens. It turned out that the dentist had a practice in the next town over from us! It was such an amazing coincidence that out of only two individuals in the entire country, one of them was in our local area. My mom called him right up and made an appointment.

This specialized blood test for observing the somatids and their evolution (as a measure of the state of the immune system) was not – and still is not – a recognized or approved procedure in the U.S. The dentist didn't really want to advertise what he was doing. He feared the legal consequences – and the very real possibility of being shut down – so he offered the test after hours.

We met with him at around 7:00 p.m. I remember how strange it felt to be waiting in a dentist's office, not for my teeth, but to have a clandestine blood test. After the dentist introduced himself, he also let me know how he felt about the metal jewelry I was wearing. He said that the human body runs on electromagnetic impulses, and rings and earrings could have a damaging effect. Then he gave me a snack made from algae.

I liked him. He was passionate about what he believed in. He took one drop of my blood and put it in a machine that showed my sample on a television screen. With my untrained eye, I tried to understand what he was seeing.

The dentist recorded the details of the test, and then he mailed the sample up to Gaston to interpret. It was about a week later when Gaston's translator called me with the results. My blood showed no symptoms of cancer! This was the news I wanted to hear!

They also told me, however, that my immune system was still weak and I should stay on the 714X for the rest of the six months. I did what they told me.

As time passed, I kept thinking, "Why are there only two people in our country trained to use this equipment? There should be one in every drugstore if it can pre-diagnose cancer – or any degenerative disease – up to two years." That was just one of many questions that would surface over the next weeks and months.

❖

The next few months were a very busy and exciting time. The story of my successful results infused new energy into the media coverage. The difference for me was, I didn't mind the attention this time! I was cured and I wanted everyone to know!

My mother had a list from the answering service of people who were calling during the day, and we would take turns returning all of their calls at night. I would tell them what I was doing: how I was giving myself the shot, all about the Essiac tea, and the kinds of foods I was eating and the vitamins I was taking.

We were invited to do follow-up interviews with people from the local TV stations as well as from shows like *Good Morning America* and *A Current Affair*, which were being shown all over the country.

I was happy to be on TV again – to let people know that my cancer was gone and that it wasn't from going back on chemotherapy.

It was from using alternative medicine.

FOURTEEN

KATIE

IT WAS APRIL, 1995. I was still taking the shot, drinking the tea and following my diet, but at the same time I was trying to get back to my normal life. There was a skate park close by and I would go there almost every day after school. Skating continued to be my best therapy.

One of the kids I skated with at the park had a younger sister who was seven years old. Her name was Katie Hartley, and this is her story.

It was the beginning of April school vacation. One day while reading to her daughter, Julie Hartley noticed that one of Katie's eyes seemed to be bulging. Julie could see the bottom, the white part. She knew that was odd.

She took Katie to the doctor and he diagnosed it as an ear infection. He prescribed medication for her, but after a day or so, her mother could still see the white of her eye. She could see that the eye was protruding, so she knew that something else had to be wrong. Julie took her daughter back to the doctor.

Katie had also started to develop a rash on her face, and they said it was probably an allergic reaction to the antibiotics. The doctors gave her Benadryl and sent them home again.

Katie's brother, Danny, was heading back to college. Julie left for a couple of days with Danny to help him get settled at school. When she returned, the problem with Katie's eye was even more pronounced.

The next morning she called the doctor's office again and requested that Katie's own pediatrician take a quick peek at her. Julie wanted someone who regularly saw Katie, and knew what she normally looked like, to evaluate her eye.

During the appointment, Katie's pediatrician called in two more doctors from the adjoining rooms at the practice to get their opinions, but none of them could figure out what was going on. They decided to send their young patient to Children's Hospital in Boston.

Julie called home to let her husband know that the doctors didn't know what was wrong, so they were sending her and Katie to Children's to see a specialist.

"Now?" he replied. "Can't it wait 'til Monday?" Paul was in the midst of building a tree house for Katie. Her eighth birthday was right around the corner.

"No, they want us to go now," Julie shrugged.

It was 3:00 p.m. on a Saturday afternoon. Julie and Katie arrived in Boston, and by about 5:00 p.m., Katie had already had numerous tests and scans. She was seen by five or six doctors, and still, nobody had said anything to Julie about what it could be.

Finally, one of the doctors who was in charge took Julie into his back office and delivered the devastating news.

"Mrs. Hartley, your daughter has a tumor and we believe that it's cancerous."

"I'll never forget it," Julie told me. "At that moment, my world came crashing down around me."

She immediately called her husband and he joined them at the hospital. Katie was admitted that night.

The tumor was the size of an orange. It was down through the jaw on her small face and reached up as high as her brain. The doctors were amazed that she never had any symptoms – no headache or anything. The tumor had pushed her nose over slightly, which her parents hadn't yet noticed. It had also pushed her eye socket out, which is what her mother had seen. Katie would need aggressive chemotherapy.

"Then came the dreaded prognosis," Julie said. "They told us she only had a 50/50 chance of survival. We were in shock."

The hospital staff stayed by their side, talking with them and counseling them all through the night and the next day.

Katie continued to have more scans, and the results were tragic news for Julie and Paul. The new images showed little foreign objects visible all over Katie's lungs. The doctors came in and told her parents that there would be no chemotherapy after all. Katie's cancer had spread. It had metastasized. They told the Hartleys that she would probably not last the week.

"We lost our minds," Julie said. "Everyone was crying. We just kept praying and praying."

There was one devoted technician, however, who spent all night showing Katie's X-rays to as many radiologists as he could find. He must have been hoping for a miracle. He reached the chief radiologist at about three o'clock in the morning, and to their astonishment, they realized that the machine they had used for the new scans – because it was brand new and highly sensitive – had picked up little particles in her that *weren't cancer.*

The Hartley's prayers were answered! The cancer had not spread!

"The doctor came back the next morning and apologized profusely to us," Julie declared, still amazed by the events that transpired. "He said they would, in fact, start chemotherapy the next day. She would have a chance at survival after all.

"Then he told us that even if the chemo and radiation didn't work, there was a well-known surgeon from Pennsylvania who might be able to operate on Katie."

Believing then that hope had been restored for their daughter, the Hartleys clung to a renewed faith.

Katie started a thirteen-month regimen of chemotherapy. The doctors told her parents that she would probably lose her hair within a couple of days. Julie felt the pangs of sadness, knowing that she would soon be seeing her little girl with no hair.

As they maintained their 'round the clock vigil at Katie's bedside, Paul and Julie were warned to wear gloves if they were touching any of her fluids. The grave situation left the three of them terrified.

Julie kept repeating to everyone at the hospital, "Please don't mention the word cancer. Katie's grandmother died of cancer. Katie is only seven years old. We just told her it's a tumor and we are going to get her help. That's how we addressed it with her."

By the first month Katie had, in fact, lost her hair. She got very sick and started to lose weight. She could no longer eat.

"We went through such horrors in those months," her mother said, "watching her get progressively worse over time. It was a nightmare."

In July, after months of chemo, Katie started the six weeks of radiation. Each time, she had to lie down on an aluminum table with a plastic mesh mask over her face. The technicians would then bolt the mask to the table so Katie couldn't move.

"She was so afraid," said Julie. "And I can't even tell you how scared I was. I think at that point I started to wonder, 'What the heck am I doing? This is just nuts.'"

At one point, one of the nurses suggested putting a feeding tube in because Katie was unable to eat. Julie and Paul were in favor of it, but the doctors fought them on the idea. Julie wondered if maybe they didn't believe Katie was going to make it. She had lost twenty pounds overall, and she was only sixty-two pounds at the beginning.

Her parents chose to have the feeding tube put in.

After nine months of the chemo and radiation, Katie's tumor was still growing and she was no better. By December, she was in the hospital most of the time. She was weak and sick from the treatments, and the doctors finally decided it wasn't fair to put her through it anymore. They told the Hartleys that they were going to discontinue the chemo.

Julie and Paul were overcome with grief. They asked the doctors about the surgery that they had discussed as a last resort, but the surgeon they had heard so much about told them that, unfortunately, the operation would not be possible. The tumor was too large in her small head.

For the second time in her short life, Katie's doctors gave her a fatal prognosis.

That January, they gave her two weeks to live.

"I think at that point I was doing a novena to the Blessed Mother every day," Julie said. "I was saying, 'What am I going to do? There has to be something I can do.'"

She opened up the phone book and started calling hospitals.

"I must have called ten or fifteen of them," she told me. "I called the National Cancer Institute, trying to find another surgeon who might be able to help. It appeared there was no solution and I was desperate for anything that might save my child."

Then Julie got a call from her sister. Her sister remembered reading an article about a boy who had used an alternative treatment for his cancer. She searched for his name, and it was Billy Best. She told Julie to call me.

They were amazed when they found out that Danny and I had been skating at the same park!

Julie laughed when she told me, "I remember the phone call so clearly because you spoke very much like my Danny. 'Yep.' 'Hello.' 'Okay.' All one-word answers."

Like I've said before, I was a quiet kid.

Julie wanted her daughter to try the same treatments I had used. Before meeting with me, Julie had started to tell Katie all about the Essiac tea and the 714X, but even though Katie was a hands-on type of kid, she wasn't onboard with the idea of getting shots. Her mom hoped that since I was close in age to Danny, Katie might relate to me and might be convinced to try it. We set up a time for them to come over to the house.

When I first saw Katie, I thought she was too far gone to be helped. She was so skinny, she couldn't even walk on her own.

When I described the treatment to her, and promised that it wasn't going to make her sick – and that with the ice, she would hardly even feel the shot – she agreed to try it.

As her mother said, "She *did* want to be involved in her treatment. At the hospital, she wanted to look in the microscope. She wanted to see the tumors. She would come out of surgery and help take all the needles out of her arm. She wanted to be a part of this."

Her parents started her on a regimen of 714X for the next seventeen months. They also took her to an acupuncturist and learned about homeopathy. They began shopping at the health food store, buying vitamins and organic fruits and vegetables just like I had done.

Katie still had her stomach tube in, so her mother juiced everything to get nutrients into her. Little by little Katie would eat tiny bits of food, and by about February she was back in school more often. She was feeling better!

In March, the Make-a-Wish Foundation gave the Hartleys a trip to Disney World and Katie had a ball. Her mother said she was out of the wheelchair for much of the trip.

Each month after that she got progressively better. She was healthier, happier. She still didn't weigh much, but she started to take on a whole new look and vitality that her parents hadn't seen in a year.

A year and a half later, in March, Julie noticed a growth in Katie's nose and she panicked. She and Paul took Katie immediately to the doctor's office where they did a scan.

Katie had been out in the waiting room while her parents were talking with the doctor.

"Paul opened the door and screamed her name," Julie said. "She came flying in and he picked her up. It was just unbelievable. She's looking at the scan. I'm crying, of course, and she says, 'I don't see it.'

"Paul said, 'That's right. It's not there.' We keep looking and looking and looking, and it's not there."

Katie's whole tumor – it had been the size of a grapefruit when the chemo was stopped – was gone!

Julie continued. "The otolaryngologist who looked at the scan was a new guy, and he was looking at it, too, saying to himself, 'Okay, what am I supposed to say to these people? I don't know what to say to them. I don't see the tumor.'

"It was completely gone."

The doctor set up a surgery appointment to see what was in Katie's nose. A couple of days later they did the surgery, and it turned out that the small growth in her nose was just scar tissue from all the radiation. They were able to remove it without incident.

They also performed several biopsies to check for cancer, and every single one of them came back negative.

Julie called Gaston's staff in Canada to tell them that the tumor was gone, and they were elated. They recommended that Katie stay on the 714X for another six months, followed by a maintenance cycle every three months. She did exactly what they said.

After a couple of years, Katie – and her mother – were both doing one cycle of twenty-one days every six months, and Katie was still taking the Essiac tea every night.

In Katie's words:

"I'm now 24 years old. It's been almost fifteen years since I saw the scans with no tumor. That day still astounds me. My mom and I both make an effort to do a cycle of 714X once a year as a form of preventive maintenance.

"I eat as healthy as I can and I visit the acupuncturist every few months. I go back to Children's and Dana Farber for yearly checkups to make sure nothing has changed.

"I am currently in the middle of having some dental surgery for nerve damage caused by the radiation. Otherwise, I have had no negative side effects since I began the 714X in 1996."

FIFTEEN

MIKE

IN HIGH SCHOOL I had a couple of friends who were in a band, and one of them – the guitar player – hosted the band practices in his basement. One day they invited me over to listen to them jam.

I had never been to this friend's house before. When I arrived, I met his parents and introduced myself. His dad must have recognized my name, and he asked me if I was the kid who had been on the news. I told him I was and I shared my story with him. He seemed more than just casually interested. After that, I headed downstairs to listen to the band.

I didn't know it that day, but my friend's father was facing a health crisis himself.

It was 1995 when I met Mike Panarelli. He was forty-six years old at the time. He was a typical hard-working married father, raising his family of four sons while juggling the demands of a busy career.

During a regular physical with his doctor and after a routine array of blood tests, some abnormal plasma cells were found in Mike's blood. The doctor called him in for some follow-up testing and to his incredulous surprise, they told him he had cancer.

He was stunned. He was a father of four active boys, and he had just been dealt the shock of his life. The doctors told him they didn't know what type of cancer he had, and they were sending him to an oncologist.

Things happened pretty quickly after that. As he tried to come to terms with what was happening, his mind was racing with all the what-if's. Before he even knew the full details of his illness, he was already thinking, "Okay, whatever I have to do, I'll just do. I'll deal with it and it'll be fine. I'll get through this."

He went in for some additional tests, including a bone marrow biopsy. He was diagnosed with multiple myeloma, a cancer of the plasma cells in bone marrow.

"Okay," he thought. "Whatever that is. We'll just kill it. We'll just get it fixed."

There wasn't time for him to even say those words aloud before the doctors crushed him with their dire prognosis. They told him he would probably live four years at most.

What Mike found out is that there is no cure for multiple myeloma. The oncologist counseled him that a double dose of chemo might help to slow the cancer's progression. Later on, a bone marrow transplant would be attempted to help ease the pain that would accompany the disease.

All of this treatment, and still Mike would not live more than a few years.

Mike requested to go to Dana Farber for the chemo. It turns out that that was a life-saving decision on his part.

"At Dana Farber," he told me, "they decided my blood was not bad enough yet to start the chemo. They didn't want me to begin it until I absolutely had to. It could cause severe side effects – complications – and even death in some people. They told me they would wait until my blood got worse.

"They estimated that I would start the chemo within a year's time," he continued.

They sent him home.

What he meant before, when he said that going to Dana Farber was a life-saving decision, was that because his chemo was deferred, he had some time to stop and think. After sitting at home awhile and wondering what the future year would hold for him, he decided, "I'm not going to just sit here and do nothing. There've gotta be some different things I can try."

That's when he contacted me and my parents. We told him how to get information on 714X, and within three or four weeks, he was using it – along with the supplements and the diet regimen that I had followed.

He also told me that reducing stress was a big part of his treatment strategy.

"I was supposed to try to work less and relax more," he said, "but how do you relax with a cancer diagnosis hanging over your head?

"I was terribly worried about my wife and my boys. What would their lives be like if I didn't survive?"

He did a complete lifestyle change. He said it was difficult to maintain a super healthy diet when others around him were enjoying all their favorite foods and beverages, but even though he didn't always like it, he stuck with it.

Mike did 714X for nine cycles the first time and he continued every two years with a maintenance cycle, which is recommended as a preventative.

From day one of his new regimen, he also drank a lot of green tea and took supplements of Vitamin C and CoQ10. (Co-enzyme Q10 is a vitamin found throughout the body, but it can also be made in a laboratory. It has many uses as a medicine and can help build up the immune system.[7])

The doctors at Dana Farber had told Mike that within four years he would not be alive, even with all their treatments. That's just how the disease progresses.

As he continued to survive year after year, surpassing even the most optimistic expectations, he had his blood tested regularly. He recalled that after nine years, his tests showed the cancer to be at a lesser level than it was when he was first diagnosed. From all indications and tests, his doctors told him the cancer was still there, but, surprisingly, it had not progressed at all – news that Mike could accept quite willingly.

"I guess I can live with that," he replied.

The doctors never offered him an explanation about why the cancer didn't advance. He told me his doctor didn't even seemed concerned enough to ask his thoughts, until his eighth annual visit. That was when Mike told him that he had been using 714X. The doctor wrote it down but stated that he had never heard of it, and Mike said he didn't seem particularly interested in the details.

"Sometimes people go through their day-to-day existence and it may seem pretty boring to them," Mike told me.

"For me," he continued, "I can count how many days I've lived since the time I was supposed to be dead, and it kind of gives you a slap on the head. Don't take life for granted, you know? I think about how my doctors gave me four years to live and what's gone on in my life since then. Being able to share these years with my family has been the greatest gift.

"When you're young and you're working all the time, you're rushing around here and there, you don't really appreciate being alive. I think everyone should get a good scare – not a cancer, but just something to make them appreciate what they have. I think people would enjoy life a little more.

"Even my kids are eating better because of my experience," he said. "They are more conscious of making healthy decisions. I couldn't really ask for more than that."

It has been *seventeen years* since Mike's cancer diagnosis in 1995 – and he was only supposed to live for *four*. His inspiring story of survival serves to remind us all not only to appreciate every single day that we have, but also to seek out solutions and take a critically active role in our own health care.

SIXTEEN

714X, ESSIAC TEA AND DIET

WHEN PEOPLE HEAR my story, they have so many questions about the treatments I used.

"What's 714X?" "You had to give yourself a shot?" "How did you learn how to do that?" "Did it hurt?" "What kind of tea was it?" "Do you still do all of this?" "What do you eat now?" – and of course, the *big* question –

"Are you afraid the cancer will come back?"

For a long time, that was the toughest one to answer.

Once we committed to trying alternative medicine, my family and I started piecing together my own little health program. I changed my diet, started drinking the Essiac tea and made plans to go to Canada.

The first thing we focused on was diet. The Essiac tea was almost as immediate, but the diet was the very first thing. That was the easiest to do right away.

We had asked my doctor if, because of the cancer, it would help me to eat certain foods or avoid certain foods, and he had assured us that there was no connection between diet and cancer. Because of that, we were puzzled why all these letters we received said that diet was so critical to healing cancer, that what you ate – or more specifically, what you *didn't* eat – could have life-changing implications.

Most of the notes and letters highlighted the same diet taboos: animal protein, sugar, white flour and dairy products. There were others that mentioned special-diet clinics, macrobiotic diets, fasting and juices, and things like that, but the majority of the letters said to eliminate those four basic things, so that's what I did.

The first to go was sugar. I basically just stopped eating anything from a package that had sugar listed as an ingredient. We starting scrutinizing all the food labels. That meant no more Mountain Dew, which was my favorite soda; I stopped drinking it "cold turkey." People used to say to me, "It must be so hard to just give up these things," and my response was, "No. What was really hard was suffering through chemotherapy." I was very willing to give up soda and other sugars if that would help. I was determined to do whatever I could to make this alternative therapy work.

I had also been drinking milk every day, and having it in my cereal, probably like every other kid in America. Since I wanted to eliminate the animal fat from my diet, we started looking for alternatives. We found soy milk, rice milk, and almond milk. I didn't really care for the taste of soy milk, but I liked the almond milk, so I drank that. My favorite milk for the cereal was the rice milk. Again, it wasn't much of a sacrifice. It was just substituting.

I started drinking eight to ten glasses of distilled water every day. Then I read that distilled was not necessarily better than plain water for daily consumption, so that was a topic of controversy. I decided to stay with the distilled water for the six months of my treatment, and then I drank spring water after that.

It helped me a lot that I was still in high school and living at home, with a schedule to keep. It was easier to be disciplined about the diet with my mother cooking for me and shopping with me. We learned to shop on the "perimeter" of the store, in other words, around the edges where all the fresh food was, and to try to reduce what we bought from the middle aisles where all the packaged food was. Those were the foods with all the additives and preservatives.

There was a TV health program on recently, and one of the questions was, "How do we really know what's in our food?" The featured guest's response was, "If it has a label on it, don't eat it." That's kind of what I was doing.

I was used to bringing my lunch to school; I never bought the school lunch because it was too expensive. My mom and I started looking at other breads besides the sliced white I had always eaten. At first we just bought a brown bread, thinking that would be enough of an improvement, and then we learned that whole wheat was healthier. We ultimately settled on Ezekiel bread, which is an organic, sprouted bread.

There were a lot of other basic changes, like brown rice instead of white. Again, the more we started to investigate, the more we learned some better ways of doing things. It's ironic, really, that nowadays people choose these foods as a regular routine for better health. When I was young, we weren't too fussy about our food choices. We pretty much ate whatever we liked. If not for my cancer, it probably wouldn't have mattered, but I had to change my ways so I could get all the vitamins and minerals possible.

Then we tried to find organic produce. A lot of people had written that organic fruits and vegetables had more nutrition, and if we could, we should try to get them. I didn't even know what organic produce was. Once we learned about it, finding it was a challenge.

We went to the supermarket and asked them, "Do you have organic produce? I'm following this special diet and I need it for my health." They didn't have it. There wasn't that much of a market for it back in the 90s. I asked them if they could get some for me, and they said, "No. Maybe try some kind of health food store." We got a little frustrated with that, but we did the best we could.

So, if we could find organic, we'd buy it. Otherwise, we at least tried to buy fruits and vegetables that were grown the closest to home, thinking they'd be the most fresh and have the most nutrients.

Organic or not, I ate a lot of fruits and vegetables, and a lot of salads. I didn't have a juicer, or anything fancy like that. I just ate the food the way it was. I didn't eat much animal protein. I did have fish once in a while.

My mother kind of had to go on a crash course discovering new things to cook for me. We learned about tofu. That was an experiment for sure. I think the first time we cooked tofu, we took it out of the package and were all looking at it wondering, what do we do with this? People had written "It's just like meat and it'll take the flavor of whatever you cook it with," so we tried it and I actually didn't mind it. One of my favorite dishes was stuffed green peppers filled with chopped tomatoes and tofu instead of meat. That was very good.

The rest of my family continued to enjoy most of the things they had always eaten. I was the one who needed the special diet, not them. I didn't mind though. I figured I'd get better soon and eventually I might go back to eating some of the things I had given up.

For years I also took a lot of vitamins and supplements. I started with Vitamin C and 50,000 IU Beta Carotene. The Vitamin C was a mega dose, 8,000 mg, that we found at a health food store. It wasn't just ascorbic acid. It was described as condensed organic fruit, with all the other enzymes and nutrients – whatever was in the orange – and it was all in this pill. It was supposed to be much better for you because it wasn't just Vitamin C, but it was all the parts of the orange working together. That's where you really got the benefit.

I'd bring those to school in my lunch box because we learned that you couldn't just take it all at once in the morning. You'd have to split it up throughout the day because it would get used up and would pass through your body. We kept learning these little things as we went along, so again, taking it properly was just another small discipline of staying on a schedule.

I used a lot of Shaklee® products. Their meal shakes are loaded with vitamins, and if I went skateboarding, I'd have an after-skateboarding-repair electrolyte drink. My mother knew a woman from church who was selling Shaklee® and that's how we learned a lot about the company. Shaklee® has a large product line of natural vitamins and non-toxic cleaning products; they've been around for many years.

As we learned more about how to boost the immune system, the list of what I took grew to include: B Vitamins, multivitamins, Energizing Soy Protein Shake, Liver DTX (Milk Thistle, Schizandra & Reishi Mushroom), Garlic, Calcium Magnesium, Nutriferon (an immune booster), and Optiflora Probiotic.

One additional thing we did was eliminate all the toxic products in our home, trying to get rid of anything that might compromise my immune system as I tried to heal.

We've been using Shaklee® cleaners, dishwashing detergent, and laundry soap for years. They are less toxic and come in concentrated form, which ends up being less expensive too.

As I mentioned, along with the changes to my diet, I started to drink the Essiac tea. As we had sat at the kitchen table, sorting through all the letters people had sent, the Essiac pile just kept growing. We figured there *had* to be something to it. One guy even sent us a sample.

When his package came, it was in a large manila envelope, without any label, and I opened it up and pulled out what looked like a bunch of grass, as if someone just pulled it out of their yard. It was a bunch of shredded herbs in a bag with directions on how to make it. I had no idea what it was, and I wasn't about to use it.

Essiac tea is made from four herbs and its purpose is to purify the blood and cleanse harmful toxins from the body. People had sent brochures for Essiac products. There were a lot of different versions of the tea, with many name variations, all claiming to be authentic. They all said they had the same four primary ingredients: burdock root, turkey rhubarb, sheep sorrel and slippery elm bark.[8] We tried the first one we could find that sounded legitimate.

We were still doing research on it, and we eventually found one company that claimed to have the original formula. That's when we actually started reading the story of the tea and where it came from, the history of it. I think someone sent us a booklet. The Internet was only in its infancy, so our research was all accomplished through letters, faxes, and through phone calls to health food stores.

It took a couple of weeks but we finally got the true, original formula. It was a powder that came in a bottle. The directions were very specific on how to make it, what kind of water to brew it with, and what kind of pot you should use. You were supposed to use distilled water, and somebody actually sent us a water distiller as a gift because they had seen my story on TV. They just said, "This is good for you. You don't want to drink tap water, so I just wanted to send you a water distiller."

It was one of my daily chores to distill the water. I'd pour two gallons of water in and it would heat up and pass through all these coils. Out would come a gallon of distilled water and then a gallon of wastewater. We used that distilled water to brew the tea and we used stainless steel pots. Aluminum wasn't allowed. Glass was okay, but we didn't have a glass pot big enough.

The routine was: Add the powder to the water; bring it to a boil; simmer for 10 minutes; turn it off for 4 hours; bring it to a boil again; simmer for 5 minutes; let it sit overnight in the 'fridge. By morning, all the sediment would kind of settle down to the bottom. We had to store it in amber bottles to protect it from the light, so it wouldn't break down. That was a big deal because it took us forever to find amber bottles.

I could make a couple of weeks' supply at a time, or maybe a little less than that because I was drinking a good amount of it. I was taking three ounces three times a day. We'd fill up all the amber bottles; the ones toward the end of the batch would be a little "chunky," a little gritty.

A lot of people said that the tea tasted horrible. To me, the chemo chemicals I had tasted were a lot worse. That stuff really frightened me. So, "horrible tasting" and "horrible smelling" is a matter of opinion. Drinking the tea felt natural to me, like if you were going to eat some bark off a tree. It was like you just shredded up some bark and mixed it with water. Not great, but doable. (And just for the record, I didn't eat bark.)

As I said, I would drink about three ounces at a time. My mother and I would start off with a little measuring cup, measuring out the three ounces, being very precise. Eventually I was just kind of free-pouring it into a glass and then "down the hatch." I could have added water to it at that point, to make it "slightly less earthy," but I figured why drink more than I have to? Just get it down.

I even brought the tea to school. I kept it cold in the refrigerator in the nurse's office. I was supposed to take it either twenty minutes before I ate or two hours after I ate, to give the tea time to pass from my upper stomach down to my lower stomach while my stomach was empty. I was in school every day, so I had to bring it with me to keep to the schedule, to keep it in my system.

I still drink it some, but not every day. The company has different products now that are concentrated, so I haven't brewed it for a long time. I would actually prefer to brew it because the concentrated version is stronger tasting, like bitters – like a tincture – but since I don't use it everyday, it would go bad if I had a big batch in my refrigerator.

So that's the story behind the tea.

The 714X was the last piece of the puzzle. 714X is a solution of camphor, nitrogen, and mineral salts that you inject directly into your lymphatic system. It works by strengthening your immune system.

I used it once a day in 21-day cycles – with two days off in between – and continued that for six months. For my kind of cancer, at the stage I was at, that was the amount that worked for me. I'm sure the treatment plans differ with every individual.

In Canada they never gave me any injections. They just gave me instruction. They had a training video I could watch too, showing the procedure.

At the beginning it was challenging. I practiced with just a glass of water – getting the water in, tapping it so all the bubbles would go to the top, making sure all the bubbles were out, and then trying to use the right amount of pressure on the syringe and timing it with a watch to see if I was doing it at the right speed.

They taught me how to find the proper landmarks on my body so I could inject it into the cluster of lymph glands in the groin area. It was just measuring along my body line – *Start here. Move two inches up, two inches over, four inches down.*

When I first started giving myself the injections, I had the lights on with everything perfect, like I was going into surgery. I usually played some quiet, soothing music during the routine. Eventually I became so comfortable with it, I could do it in the dark.

I'd give myself the shot right when I woke up. It would fit into my schedule best that way. It's funny; it gave me a sense of accomplishment throughout the day, like I'd completed something really important first thing in the morning. It was a positive thing for me. I really embraced it.

After about a week, I felt a hundred percent. I was out skateboarding, being active. I began treatments on January 10, 1995. Around the third week of March, I came back to the hospital for tests and the cancer was – well, you know by now – gone! Now I do a 21-day cycle once a year.

When I hit my 20s, I was feeling great, working at bars and clubs, and hanging out late at night. I admit it was "party time" for a long time. I kind of fell off the healthy eating regimen for a while. Maybe I was feeling entitled to rebel against all the discipline, all the seriousness. I had a good time.

I have since settled down and I think that now I probably eat on the healthier side of normal, mostly because of all I've learned about food and nutrition. I still eat sprouted or whole wheat bread, but not too much bread overall. I eat a lot of fruits and vegetables, especially when I'm working. I eat a lot of beans and nuts and I do eat some organic eggs and meat; I just try not to eat too much meat. I know organic foods are more expensive, but I feel a lot better about eating them. When I can afford to buy them, I do.

I work at a natural foods/organic foods store now, and I still enjoy learning about the food I eat and finding out where it is grown or raised. Part of my job is to buy organic produce from local farms, and I enjoy talking about it to people who come in to shop. Just staying close to that connection with food is great.

Several years after I was cured, I started to cut back on the vitamins and supplements that had been part of my daily routine. I eventually stopped taking them; I guess I got tired of it all because I had used so many for so long.

I did decide recently to go back to a multivitamin. I figure it's probably a good idea to help get whatever nutrients I might be missing from my diet, so I take one of those every day. I try to eat well, sleep well, and just enjoy.

I always got a lot of exercise from skateboarding. It really helped sustain me through the stress of having cancer, through the running away – everything. My jobs have always been very physical too. For years I worked in bars, both as a bartender and a barback. With that kind of work, you're "sweat through" by the end of the night.

I believe 714X is keeping my immune system healthy, and that's why I continue to use it. I believe that my health is a balance and it's never going to hurt to try to help keep that balance. I come across stresses every day, whether they're environmental, emotional, food-related, sleep-related – so many things. So, I try to keep my immune system strong.

Gaston doesn't tell me that if I stop using 714X, my cancer will come back; he never says anything like that. However, he does say that cancer cells are present in all of us all the time, and this is a product that helps regulate the immune system, keeping it at its best. He doesn't have cancer, and he never has, but he uses 714X himself. He's in his late eighties and he's still in the lab everyday.

People always want to know, "Are you afraid the cancer will come back?"

The honest answer is no, I'm not. Not any more. It has been gone for a long time.

I had many check-ups early on after my cancer was gone, and there was never any more sign of it. I eventually felt I could stop worrying about it. I do still get my blood tested every few years or so whenever I have the opportunity to go up to Canada, just to verify the overall health of my blood.

I haven't been getting regular physicals here in the U.S., mostly because the types of jobs I've held over the years didn't offer any health insurance – a situation I find ironic considering my medical history.

I finally have coverage through my current workplace, so in the future I might be more inclined to follow a traditional schedule of "wellness" visits. I like the sound of that.

SEVENTEEN

SPREAD THE WORD

THANKFULLY, THROUGHOUT THE eighteen years since my cancer has been gone, the news media has continued to have an interest in me and in my story – helping me spread the word about surviving cancer and about the treatments I chose. Back in the 90s when the story broke, programs about my success with alternative medicine aired on *20/20, CNN, Inside Edition,* NBC's *Dateline,* and others. It was amazing to me to have so much attention!

Over the next ten years, I had many opportunities to do more interviews – either for magazines, newspapers, radio or TV. It made me appreciate how important the story of treating cancer is.

About a month after I returned home from running away to Texas, I did a second TV interview for *A Current Affair.* They wanted to wrap up their original "runaway" story with a follow-up to see how I was doing.

They offered to send Heather and DeeDee up from Houston to visit me. It was around Christmas time, 1994, and the next thing I knew, the producers put the two of them on a plane and arranged the whole visit.

The girls stayed with me at my house for about a week, which gave me the opportunity to introduce them around to some of my friends at home. My skateboarding buddies from Texas weren't too happy, however, that the news program didn't include them in the trip.

My very first speaking engagement was a few months later, back in Houston. It was April 17, 1995 at Rice University, the Hanszen College Aaron Seriff Lecture Series. Somebody from there gave me a call and asked if I would come talk about my experience. They flew me down there and I stayed in one of the dorms. My parents didn't attend; it was just me. It was my first time staying at a college (and going to a college party!). I had a great time.

I also testified in the fall later that year, in October, before a Massachusetts State House Committee on alternative medicine. Someone had called us to let us know it was going on and to say that we should probably show up; obviously my part in it wasn't anything too formal. Everyone was still learning about alternative medicine at that point, so my short speech was very general. I just said I was thankful that I was able to find and use alternative medicine, and was grateful that I had the freedom to use the treatment of my choice.

September 1995 - Speaking at the Cancer Control Society
Alternative Therapy Convention. I was seventeen.

One of my other early speaking engagements was that same
fall, in September. I was seventeen. It was one of the biggest
conferences I would ever attend and it was held at the Cancer
Control Society in Pasadena, California. (I would return to this
conference two more times in September of '98 and '99.)

Cancer survivors were invited to attend to tell their success
stories. The organizers contacted me and offered to fly me and

my parents out there. I spoke in front of several hundred people and I remember being pretty nervous.

It was there that I met a woman named Charlotte Gerson, author and founder of the *Gerson Institute* in California. In the 1920s her father, Max Gerson, M.D., introduced a natural treatment for disease that floods the body with nutrients. His treatments used "intensive detoxification to eliminate wastes, reactivate the immune system and restore the body's essential defenses."[12]

The *Gerson Institute* Web site states, "It is rare to find cancer, arthritis, or other degenerative diseases in cultures considered 'primitive' by Western civilization. Is it because of diet? The fact that degenerative diseases appear in these cultures only when modern packaged foods and additives are introduced would certainly support that idea. Max Gerson said, 'Stay close to nature and its eternal laws will protect you.' "[13]

I was fascinated to learn about the Institute because its treatments were very parallel to what I had started doing when I chose a natural cure. I, too, was maintaining an organic diet as much as possible and was reducing the toxins in my environment. It helped confirm for me that some of these alternative treatments should have a real place in modern medicine and should be available to people who want to try them.

At the conference, I also met former Iowa congressman, Berkley Bedell. He had used 714X and other alternative medicine to treat his own cancer and lyme disease. Because of these personal health crises, Bedell was passionate about pursuing all types of alternative therapies.

Using his Washington status, Bedell had "created the Office of Alternative Medicine with Senator Tom Harkin (D-Iowa) within the National Institutes of Health (NIH) to investigate and validate promising alternative therapies. Despite this milestone, their efforts were frustrated by bureaucratic and scientific inertia."[14]

After making no progress with the government, Bedell launched the Foundation for Alternative and Integrative Medicine (FAIM) "with a mission to identify breakthrough complementary and alternative therapies and to research and report on their effectiveness. FAIM's mission also places importance upon the affordability of treatments in the belief that the world needs cost-effective solutions to bring health to the greatest number of people."[15]

In addition to the American presenters at the conference, there were many doctors in attendance from Mexico. At their clinics, therapies are offered that aren't necessarily approved in this country. Many Americans travel to Mexico for alternative medicine even if their insurance won't cover the costs and they have to pay out-of-pocket.

One of the sponsoring hospitals was the *Oasis of Hope*, founded in 1963 by Dr. Ernesto Contreras. It was his son, Dr. Francisco Contreras, who paid for my parents and me to fly out to the Pasadena conference.

To quote their Web site, Dr. Ernesto Contreras "began a healing tradition known as the Total Cancer Treatment Care Approach. Dr. Contreras has been recognized in multiple publications as a pioneer in body, mind and spirit medicine. He taught his medical staff to never prescribe cancer treatments that would destroy the patient's quality of life. He also insisted that *Oasis of Hope* physicians offer therapies that they would be willing to take themselves. The integration of conventional complementary therapies with emotional and spiritual counseling, along with his emphasis on the doctor-patient relationship are the principle reasons why more than 100,000 patients from 55 nations have come to *Oasis of Hope* for cancer treatment in the last 45 years."[16]

I was so inspired talking to Dr. Contreras. After hearing me speak, he generously offered me an open invitation to come to his hospital to learn about his treatments – sort of as an internship opportunity. A few years later, I would gratefully take him up on that offer.

In 1997, one of the TV shows we did was called *In Person with Maureen O'Boyle*. My father and I were invited on the talk show that O'Boyle hosted from 1996 to 1997. I was nineteen. I think the episode was one of her last shows and they probably wanted to spice it up, so they got us on there and she led a discussion about alternative medicine and "why the government isn't telling us about these cancer cures."

We were the first guests, talking about 714X and Essiac tea. Then she had Dr. Joe Gold from the Syracuse Cancer Research Institute come on as well. He was promoting hydrazine sulfate as a cancer treatment, and there was a lot of controversy about its effectiveness.

Dr. Gold's therapy came into the spotlight around that time because there were articles about it in *Penthouse Magazine*. The wife and business partner of Bob Guccione, publisher of *Penthouse,* used hydrazine sulfate in an attempt to treat her breast cancer.[9]

I know that the purpose of the show was probably just to present something controversial to get a rise out of the audience and to "up" the ratings. They weren't going to support or validate any particular treatment, but as I've said before, if I got a chance to use the media to tell my story, I took it.

Another interview, in '98 or '99, was for a story on Charlie Pixley with reporters from the program *Extra*. At the time, we were communicating with Charlie and had begun a relationship with him. Charlie is the man I referred to earlier who mailed us the grey notebook, *Do No Harm* – the book that helped confirm my instinct to use 714X.

Charlie's story is well-publicized. He believed in 714X and in Gaston Naessens' science. Charlie wanted to help distribute this alternative compound to people in the U.S. who perhaps had exhausted all conventional medical treatment and had no other hope. He wanted Americans to have the same access to it that the terminally ill in Canada did – in the Emergency Release Program – so he began selling 714X out of his research facility in New York.

Selling 714X in the U.S., however, was against the law because the drug was not FDA approved. They raided his office, took all of his computers, monitors, files, keyboards, patient records

– everything. "Pixley was found guilty of inter-commerce and was sentenced to nineteen years in prison. His sentence was later reduced on appeal to a year and a month, partly, he feels, because he was allowed to present arguments detailing the government's suppression of non-orthodox therapies."[17]

My statement in the interview was basically just that I didn't believe it was right for Charlie to go to prison, and I genuinely thanked him for what he did for me, helping me learn about 714X.

In June of 1999 when I was twenty one, I spoke at a conference in Virginia: *Comprehensive Cancer Care: Integrating Complementary and Alternative Therapies.* It was for medical professionals, to raise awareness of all kinds of natural therapies. There were many booths with exhibitors and different technologies being presented. I was thrilled to see so many supporters of alternative methods.

I was invited to speak and I was assigned to a panel discussion with author and lawyer, Michael Cohen. He had written a book called *The Practice of Integrative Medicine.* He was the first speaker and I was next to him: the cancer survivor with personal experience with 714X, Essiac tea and diet. Next to me was the head of the FDA, followed by a board certified oncologist, a board certified radiologist, and several others.

We each had ten or fifteen minutes to speak and then our turn was over. Right after me, the next speaker – from the FDA – said, "A little bit of knowledge can be the most dangerous

June, 1999 at the Comprehensive Cancer Care Conference in Virginia
sponsored by the National Cancer Institute and the
Center for Mind/Body Medicine

thing." In other words, that I had a little bit of knowledge. And I can totally agree with him, that if you give someone the tiniest bit of knowledge, they might run wild with it and go in the wrong direction. But in my heart from what I went through, I did not feel that was the case. Unfortunately, I couldn't comment on his remarks because my turn was over.

The crowd did not like his response to me. There was some booing out there in the audience. So, imagine me, at that age, getting such a supportive response from a distinguished crowd like that. It made a big impression on me and it made me want to continue speaking whenever I could.

I also met Dr. James Gordon at that conference. He is the Founder and Director of The Center for Mind-Body Medicine.[10] He signed his book, *Manifesto for a New Medicine, Your Guide to Healing Partnerships and the Wise Use of Alternative Therapies*, and gave it to me. He said, "Follow your heart," and he gave me encouraging words. He was the Chair of the White House Commission on Complementary and Alternative Medicine Policy[11] under President Clinton, and I saw him in *National Geographic* magazine years later on a mission to fight disease and famine in other countries. I will never forget meeting him that day.

There was a convention in Philadelphia that I attended. The Philadelphia area had some strong supporters of natural medicine and natural healing.

It was the same thing; I was the cancer survivor who used natural medicine. The event really ended on a high note because after the presentation, there was a question and answer period at the back of the room, and a swarm of people lined up to meet me, saying "Wow," and to tell me how awesome the story was.

In my early 20s, I was living and working on the North Shore (the coastal area of Massachusetts between Boston and New Hampshire). I lived in Swampscott for a while. As I mentioned before, I worked in a couple of restaurants, bartending and barbacking. I actually liked barbacking best because it was more just running around and lifting, weaving through crowds, up and down stairs. Bartending was good, too, because I could have seven conversations going at once while working.

It's funny. My qualification for bartending was that I was tall. They said, "You don't look like a fighter, so you're not going to be a bouncer. You're tall and you're good looking, so get behind the bar." I said, "Okay," and that's where I was for a few years.

I eventually felt that I was not fulfilling my potential, that I should be doing something more important – something that I cared about. I had been through so much, and settling in to a routine job was very difficult for me. I had a talk with my bosses and told them I wasn't happy. I needed to do something else.

Since I had chosen a path of alternative medicine for myself, I was motivated to continue learning anything I could about treatments and ideas that were outside of the mainstream. I kept thinking about Dr. Contreras, his hospital in Mexico, and his invitation to come and see what they were all about.

So, again, I jumped on a Greyhound bus and off I went to Mexico. I stayed at *Oasis of Hope* for a month and they put me to work in public relations. The entire staff and all the doctors were Mexican, and there were a lot of Americans coming through the door. My job was to welcome people into the hospital, give them tours, and try to answer as many questions as I could.

While I was there, I did a little studying about their philosophies and methods. I had opportunities to meet and talk with many different people suffering from all types of cancer. It was a great experience, just to learn and absorb information from a thriving alternative medical community.

I did a juice fast while I was there. It was ten days of no eating – just drinking juices – and it was very intense and very cleansing. I felt incredibly good at the end of it, tranquil almost, and so clearheaded.

I remember the effect it had on me mentally and physically because I was hitting all my skateboarding tricks. Normally, when you start running through your tricks, some tricks will work perfectly and others you'll miss. You don't typically "hit" them all.

Well, after the fast, I was landing every single trick – everything I tried, everything I could think of. I felt efficient and powerful, like my body was functioning at an optimal level and I had received all the nutrients I needed with no excess left over to bog me down.

I came home from Mexico and went back to working. I was still struggling to find my "right" place. My mother and I started a cancer support group in September, 2001 and we continued that for six years. My mother had also started a home business distributing information about the therapies and nutritional supplements that I used for my treatment.

She still hosts that original Web site (BillyBest.net) and anyone who is looking for information about alternative medicine can go there and contact us.

This was another *48 Hours* interview
(circa 2003) in Myrtle Beach, South Carolina
where my parents were living.

I have since launched an additional site to accompany this book. The address is www.TheBillyBestStory.com, and people can email me directly through that site.

After the trip to Mexico, I was in touch with a friend of mine who was living in Vail, Colorado and he was about to move on from there. In his words, he had "outgrown the mountain," and was headed to Whistler, Canada.

He had been very popular in his Vail community, and I was able to move in there sort of on his "coattails." A buddy of mine came along with me and we were warmly welcomed. It was easy enough for us to get work for the season so we just moved in.

We both got jobs in ski shops and we rented rooms in a huge house on the back side of the mountain. One of the ski runs came out right at our back yard. We used to take the series of lifts all the way to the top and then follow the trails down to our house. We'd run into herds of elk running off to the side of us as we were flying down the mountain on our snowboards. We were there for one season, from October until April or May, working and snowboarding until it was time to return home.

While I was in Vail, I did an interview for the news program *48 Hours.* They had contacted my parents and wanted to do a follow-up story on me. Since I had moved out West, they came out there to produce the story. My dad had a business trip to make to Colorado, so he and my mom came out for the interview too.

My parents and I didn't initiate any of these interviews, but because of all the publicity we'd had over the years, we knew several TV producers and we had spent a lot of time with some of them. I guess they felt that the story was worth following.

There was another significant interview that we did related to the lawsuit that the Naessens' were pursing against Dana Farber for an alleged breach of contract.

In 1999, Naessens' company, CERBE Distribution, hired Dana Farber researchers to conduct in-vitro laboratory tests of 714X.

In a letter to Dana Farber's Director of Research that was later leaked to the media, two of the Dana Farber researchers involved in the 714X test wrote,

> "For the first time, our data provide scientific evidence supporting that 714X is an immune stimulus...714X is thought to elevate the immune response and have some role in killing tumor cells. Our data provide evidence to support this theory."[18]

> According to the *Boston Herald* (May 21, 2001), the researchers wrote that their preliminary "test results 'clearly demonstrate' that 714X activates white blood cells and induces the secretion of proteins that play a role in the body's immune defense system, including the part of the immune system that recognizes tumor cells."[19]

Not long after the 714X tests began in 1999, in spite of the promise of these early results, the testing was shut down by Dana Farber. CERBE sued Dana Farber for breach of contract, alleging that, although the tests showed "positive chemokine reactivity" for 714X, Dana Farber prematurely ended the tests.

In mid-2000, the suit was settled out of court and a confidentiality agreement prohibits both Dana Farber and CERBE from discussing the case.[20]

❖

While that lawsuit story was in the news, Caterina Bandini, who was an anchor at WHDH Boston Channel 7, contacted us and wanted to get our take on it.

Usually the reporters would come in and bang out a story in maybe two or three visits over a week, a week and a half. This time, however, Caterina spent about a month on it, and we felt that her report was a fair and very thorough assessment of what we had been doing. She clearly stated that, "These people have been through a crisis. They found out about this natural medicine and it worked."

She spent all that time and the story was supposed to air on Valentine's Day. My family and I were all sitting around the TV that evening, and literally less than ten minutes before the show was scheduled to air, we got a call from Caterina and she was really upset. They weren't going to run the show.

It was our impression that the show was scrapped at the last minute because of a potential concern by the network of repercussions regarding advertising dollars from the pharmaceutical industry.

So that was the frustration. We had all been through such a difficult time. Having cancer. Going through chemo. Deciding not to do it. Finding another way. Getting better. Being so hopeful that we would have the opportunity to share what we had learned with other people – and then having that hope taken away.

That was pretty much the moment when I realized that getting the word out was going to have to continue to be a grassroots effort. So, whenever there was an offer to speak somewhere, I'd go. I was never paid to speak, but I would always go. We decided we would just keep doing what we were doing, keeping the Web site open and being available to talk about it anytime anyone needed us.

I was recently invited to speak at Harvard Medical School in Boston, Massachusetts – in February of 2012. Students in a class entitled "Ethics of Chemotherapy" were studying my story and they asked me if I would come in. I was really happy to have the opportunity to share some of my thoughts with these medical students, and to tell them about my experience with 714X – without the hype and without any misinformation that is floating out there.

After I recited a short summary of my history, they asked some great questions. The following are some excerpts from that question and answer period (*which have been edited for this publication*).

> *When you got all the feedback from people on alternative treatments, did you also get mail from people who had done chemo successfully?*
>
> I did, and they said, "You can do it, Billy. Just hang in there. Put your mind somewhere else. Give the doctors a year of your life, and you'll have the rest of it." There were a lot of people like that. Very supportive.

Then there were also people who wrote, "You're so ungrateful. My brother had cancer and his was Stage 4. If he was Stage 2A like you were and he had had the option of taking chemotherapy, he'd be alive now." People were passionate about it either way.

For me, in my heart, I didn't feel chemo was right for me at that time. After reading all the letters and considering the options, I still felt that building my immune system up was a better choice than using a toxic treatment. I am half Native American, and maybe that had something to do with it, some kind of inner spirit leading me. I'm not sure.

We were discussing how would we react if we had a family who came in with their son and said they didn't want to do chemo anymore for this relatively treatable cancer. We were talking about what factors would play into our decision for how to respond.

One of the factors would be that they would have to exhibit competency, showing that they fully understood both their disease and the risks and benefits of treatment. If the patient is only sixteen, how do you decide whether that young person understands the risks?

How can you tell if someone at a certain age is capable of making that decision? I would say that's very difficult, and I wouldn't say that you can just put a number on it. In some cultures, a boy of thirteen is considered a man. It depends on the person. There should be a lot

At Harvard Medical School, February 2012

of communication up front, evaluating the ability of the patient to understand, to know the consequences, to determine the support of his family, and finally, to attempt to understand his beliefs – if he has any yet.

I'm also curious if you had any depression at that time along with your illness? We talked about whether that would impact your decision.

I was really not emotional. I just took it for what it was. You know, we're all here. We're all going to die.

I've made it this far, so at least be grateful for that. I just accepted that, yes, I might die sooner than the next guy. So I was trying to take advantage of what time I had left. Just feel well and enjoy it.

Why do you think doctors haven't gotten behind 714X?

There have been no clinical trials done on 714X. Doctors can't talk about it because they don't know about it, and they don't know about it because there have been no studies done on it. Back in 2002 or so, Dana Farber was getting a lot of phone calls. People were saying, "What's up with this kid? What's up with this 714X? He got better. How come we don't know about this?"

What is in the 714X treatment?

714X is not a drug; it's an immune regulator which can speed up or slow down the immune system, depending on what the body needs. It's a solution of camphor, nitrogen, and mineral salts and you inject it directly into your lymphatic system. It's not cancer specific. They claim that any degenerative disease of the immune system can be helped by it. They are working with AIDS patients trying this out. No clinical trials have been done.

We went down to the NCI (National Cancer Institute) in 2005 or 2006 with our case. The Naessenses sent sixteen cases and all of their records to the NCI. The NCI selected five people for the Best Case Series.

The Best Case Series is a program that the National Cancer Institute developed for evaluating data from complementary and alternative medicine. The science is required to involve the same rigorous methods used to evaluate treatment responses from conventional medicine.[21]

After two years of research on our personal histories and our success with 714X, they found that there wasn't enough data to warrant further testing on it, so the case was closed. That was our opportunity to try to begin clinical trials, but it didn't happen.

Do you know other people who this treatment has worked for?

Yes, I've known a few personally. I'd like to know more, but unfortunately, there's no database of people who've tried it. The first two people I knew had amazing recoveries. I know there are people who haven't survived, but I also don't have people calling up, saying, "Hey, I'm still doing well from that 714X." It would be great if we could create a network of people who can discuss 714X and say, "I did use this and it's worked for this many years and these are my experiences with it." Maybe this book will help with that goal.

The first time I ever heard about 714X was from a kid in my high school. He was the one person who I confided in about my cancer way back in the beginning. It was the very day that I got my diagnosis, and I was skateboarding in the supermarket parking lot, trying to clear my head. I went into the store, just flipping through magazines, and he came over to me.

"Oh, you have cancer. That's a bummer. My mom had cancer and – your doctors might not want me to tell you this but – she used this experimental therapy from Canada."

He didn't name it at the time because I didn't give him the opportunity. I wasn't ready to hear it.

About a year later, I found out that what she was using was 714X, so I approached him, "Can I talk to her about it? Would she be willing to talk to other people?"

He said, "No. Because it's not approved. It's illegal and she's afraid the FDA is going to come and take it away, and she still needs it." So I believe there's that fear of not being able to get it that keeps people from sharing their experiences.

But think about this. The only kid I confided in about my cancer just happened to have a mother using 714X for hers.

We know that so many of the treatments that we have that are FDA approved came from herbs or plants or fish. Did any of your doctors present it to you like that?

Did any of them embrace the concept of natural remedies as an adjunct to their therapy? I'm wondering if that would have made a difference in your willingness to compromise.

No, they didn't, and that might have helped. If I felt like they were sitting on the same side of the table with me, instead of sitting "up" and talking "down" to a sixteen year old, especially when I brought information about herbs and diet, that might have helped.

It was a painful time for my family. We were already in a healing crisis, and we didn't need to be in a fight with our doctors. But I'm not sorry I followed the treatment I chose. And if I hadn't run away, I would probably never have found out about any of these alternatives. I believe I am healthier because of it.

Obviously, I'm not a doctor; I also don't go around recommending 714X to everyone I meet who has cancer. I know there are all different types and stages of cancer and I wouldn't ever claim that what cured me could cure everyone else. People should always consult their own doctors to figure out what will work for them.

If I ever become seriously ill again, I will certainly want to consider whatever the latest treatments are and hopefully work *with* my doctors, this time as an adult. I would also want the freedom of choice to supplement traditional therapy.

I just hope that people can learn about alternative options ahead of time so that, God forbid, if they ever do develop cancer, or someone they love develops cancer, they'll know they have options.

I'm hoping that by writing this book, I will reach more people and spread the word. If nothing else, maybe 714X could play a role as a final therapy, when chemo treatment has been exhausted and the doctors have said, "Sorry. There's nothing more we can do."

People want to know if there's anything else possible, even if it's just for better quality of life for the last few months. They don't want anyone to give up on them.

I have a son of my own now, and that's a miracle that I thought would probably not happen for me. One of the side effects of chemo is infertility and I didn't leave a sperm donation before beginning those treatments. I didn't think I was going to live that long.

Having a child kind of sparked me into getting back to telling my story – that, and the report a few years ago of a young boy who ran away to avoid chemotherapy for his cancer.

That story sounded just a little too familiar.

EIGHTEEN

THE NEXT CHAPTER

WHEN MY STORY came out in '94, there were a few other teens in the news going through similar circumstances. Those reports opened up a whole dialog within the American Medical Association (AMA) and between doctors around the country about how to better communicate with teens and help empower them to be part of their care.

In the *New York Times*, dated 11/10/94, the Director of the Department of Adolescent Health of the AMA said that this brings up the question of "ethical and practical issues about a teenager's role in determining medical care."[22]

The Director of the Center for Bioethics at the University of Pennsylvania said, "I do think teenagers have the right to refuse treatment, and it makes sense to determine teenagers' competence in these cases." He also said, though, that just because they refuse treatment doesn't mean you stop trying to convince them to continue.[23]

In the first ten years after my cancer was gone, when I participated in so many speaking engagements around the country, I felt like a lot of attention had been focused on my success with 714X. I thought that surely some progress would be made by the medical community in researching it. When I eventually realized that that wasn't happening, I became kind of despondent about the whole thing and I stopped talking about it.

Then in 2009, a new story hit the papers about an even younger boy, from the Midwest, who tried to refuse chemo for his cancer. His mother wanted him to use alternative treatments and she ran away with him. The courts overruled them based on the boy's age and his determined level of competency, and they ordered him back to the hospital for the traditional therapy.

That young boy's story reminded me that the debate over minors' rights rages on. It renewed a desire in me to finally finish this book that I had started over a decade ago, and to keep talking, keep advocating for the right to choose alternative treatments.

Cancer is a formidable opponent – an ugly, menacing monster. For me, being able to wage a fight against it with the weapons of my choice? That's been the ultimate win.

It's been eighteen years since I beat cancer, and I know there are countless other people – like Katie and Mike – who've done the same thing.

I haven't just won my *battle* with cancer.

I've won my war.

Julia Cumes

Coast Guard Beach, Cape Cod National Seashore, Eastham, MA

ENDNOTES

1. The Patriot Ledger, *To public, boy's life becomes a runaway sensation,* 11/23/94

2. The Patriot Ledger, *Search for son a lonely task,* 11/5/94

3. ojibwatea.com/essiac_ojibwateafaq.php

4. *The Story of Essiac, Her Healing Journey,* Rene M. Caisse R.N., 1977

5. quotations.hubpages.com/hub/Essiac-Tea-Does-It-Work-For-Cancer

6. The Caledonian Record, *Health Beat,* St. Johnsbury, VT, Maria Chaloux, 2/8/96

7. webmd.com

8. natural-cures-and-home-remedies.com/essiac-tea-ingredients.html

9. en.wikipedia.org/wiki/Hydrazine_sulfate

10. integrativepractitioner.com/article_ektid830.aspx

11. integrativepractitioner.com/article.aspx?id=10672

12. gerson.org/GersonTherapy/gersontherapy.htm

13. Ibid

14. faim.org/about/berkleybedell.html

15. Ibid

16. oasisofhope.com/about_us.php

17. uts.cc.utexas.edu/~wbova/fn/gov/714X.pdf

18. health.groups.yahoo.com/group/Cancer_alternatives/message/383

19. Ibid

20. Ibid

21. cancer.gov/cam/bestcase_intro.html

22. The Patriot Ledger, *Teens Need Voice in Treatment*, Gail Slap and Martha Jablow, New York Times News Service, 11/10/94

23. Ibid

"How did you meet?"

Over the many months that I've worked on *THE BILLY BEST STORY*, I've mentioned it to people along the way, and they've often asked me, "How did this all begin? How did you meet?"

This is how it happened.

In April 2011, I read about a memoir writing workshop being held at the Sandwich Library (Sandwich, Massachusetts). I decided that the workshop could be a good networking opportunity for my business, and I might also get some writing tips, so I went. The event was hosted by a husband and wife, both authors, from Western Mass. After their presentation, they opened up the floor for a short question and answer period.

It was clear from the various questions being asked that the audience members were all writing their own memoirs. There was one young woman, however, sitting just behind me, who stood up and said something like, "My boyfriend has a story to tell. He's been in the media. He's been on TV. How does someone find a writer to help them write their story?"

As I listened to her speak, I reached my hand into my pocket and felt the small stack of business cards I had put there. I thought to myself, "As soon as she finishes with her question, I am going to hand her my card," and that's exactly what I did. Almost immediately after that, she had to leave the room in a hurry, so I didn't even get a chance to speak with her. I didn't know Billy's name yet. I didn't know his story or anything about him.

It took a few months, but I received an email from Billy Best. I called him and he started to explain who he was and what his story was about. He said, "You can Google me." Well, I did Google him and right away, I loved his story. I knew I wanted to work on it.

It has been my privilege and my extreme pleasure to work with Billy on his amazing story and to help him deliver it to the world.

Linda Conti
Sandcastle Memoirs

Sandcastle
MEMOIRS
Life Stories Recorded and Written

THE NEXT BOOK

A YOUNG BOY thrills in racing through the woods, leaping over stumps and rocks as he makes his way through the trees. He moves with fluid grace, his long, dark hair slapping against his naked back. As he rushes by the familiar pockets of dense brush, he scans for wild beasts or any other hostile threats that could be lurking.

He safely approaches the edge of the dark canopy and slows his pace as he reaches the clearing. He momentarily squints from the bright sun, feeling his heart pounding in his chest. He feels free and alive – a kinship with the earth, the sun, and the wind.

He runs up the back steps into the house and stops in the kitchen, grabbing a glass of water from the tap. His dad is there, and Billy decides to share his latest revelation with his father.

"Hey Dad? I think I'm an Indian," he states matter-of-factly as he gulps down the water while still trying to catch his breath.

"I love running through the woods. I'm always dreaming that I'm taking off my clothes and running through the woods – like an Indian.

"So, I think that's what I am."

His father peers at him over the newspaper.

"You're not an Indian, son," he replies with a kind smile and a shake of his head. "You're French.

"Your relatives were French and that's why your skin is a little darker than ours. That's all. French. Not Indian."

Billy briefly considers this information from his father, but ultimately he is undeterred. He continues to dream his dreams and hopes that maybe someday – *somehow* – he will know for certain his true heritage.

Watch for our next book – the continuing true story of Billy Best and his search for his Native American roots.